# TOO
# MUCH
# W🌍RLD

# TOO
# MUCH
# WRLD

How I survive as an autistic girl

Claire Murphy

CHAPLIN BOOKS

www.chaplinbooks.co.uk

First published in 2020 by Chaplin Books

Copyright © Claire Murphy

ISBN: 978-1-911105-50-3

A CIP catalogue record for this book is available from The British Library

Illustrations by Claire Murphy and Jackie Murphy

Printed by Imprint Digital

Chaplin Books
5 Carlton Way
Gosport PO12 1LN
Tel: 023 9252 9020
www.chaplinbooks.co.uk

*Too Much World* is dedicated to my mum and dad for making me who I am, and to my therapist Dr Abbie Tolland, for helping me to finally *understand* who I am, and for giving me the confidence and knowledge to write this book to help more people understand autism in girls and women. It is also dedicated to all the 'lost girls'.

# Contents

# Foreword

I am 33 years old and I was diagnosed with Autism Spectrum Disorder two years ago. The diagnosis was one of the most significant things ever to happen to me, because it made my life make sense. It was like finally finding a pair of shoes that fit me, so I could start to walk forward in life more comfortably, with the right support at last. To my relief, the complex combination of difficulties I had *forever* fought to hide had one name: autism.

That meant that I am not alone after all. Nor am I 'less'. There is an explanation for why I'm the way I am and a whole community of other people that experience the world as I do.

Since my private diagnosis (made possible with the financial support of my parents) I have felt less pressure to disguise myself. For the first time in my life, I am learning to ask for help. I am starting to say 'no', something that has never occurred to me to do before. This is making a big difference to my health in many ways. But knowing the name of my condition does not mean that I, and the people I'm closest to, understand everything about it. It doesn't erase my difficulties or excuse me from making a positive contribution to society.

> *Knowing the name of my condition is simply a step toward learning how to manage my difficulties and find out what works for me, so that I can contribute to society more successfully.*

As with any invisible disability, adapting my environment, and learning and communicating my needs without the shame of difference and fear of judgment, is hard. This is true for humans on all 'spectrums', from disability to phobia, age, weight, gender, sexuality, intelligence, pain, food intolerance, sensitivity, fitness, mental health, wealth … anything. As humans, we need to learn how to look after one another through life as it becomes more and more complicated, and focus on a person's goodness. We have no idea what other people are going through, what they are hiding, and what realities they experience. We cannot know unless we open our minds and make people feel that they can tell us.

Writing is my quest toward understanding how autism, combined with my personality type, affects me. It is an opportunity for me to discover how I 'work' in order to try and live the rest of my life more successfully.

Doctors and psychiatrists are skilled at identifying and diagnosing conditions, but the support to unpick and understand those conditions isn't always there.

Writing has helped me and I realised that my writing could help more people than just me.

If I had been diagnosed with autism earlier in life, I may have received the support I needed to live as a confident, knowledgeable autistic person, rather than a failing neuro-typical: living as opposed to surviving. But along with my teachers, family and friends, I had no idea about how autism can present itself in girls growing up in the 1990s. Especially shy, 'average' girls with acute self-awareness. Autism is normal: a gift, a blessing, if you (and the rest of society) truly understand, accept and manage it. But un-diagnosed autism, un-*managed* autism, or autism accompanied by mental health disorders, is a killer. This is increasingly inevitable in autistic people who are 'missed,' and autistic people who desperately compete to fit into a world that simply was not built to accommodate them.

My friend Lesley, who I met at the very first rehearsal of a new community choir called *Sing Now Choir*, taught me that we *all* become better when we share. It was Lesley, and her mum, Barbie Smith, who inspired me to share my writing so that I could provide the 'survival guide' that I never had. I needed to give people the opportunity to see the world from the perspective of an autistic, professional woman. I needed to write, with my three younger siblings in mind, to give others the tools and knowledge to reach the point of diagnosis or self-diagnosis, in a more healthy and informed way than I had done.

It was hard at first.

Sharing things about myself is something I never had the confidence to do before my diagnosis of autism. But all humans have strengths and weaknesses. We all need support with something. What tends to happen when we share the most difficult things is that – despite our diagnoses or eccentricities – we discover that *we're not that different from one another after all.*

Nothing I have written in this book is based on research, but on candid life experience. I cannot write for everyone with autism, or everyone with mental health problems. I can only write for me, as a coping mechanism, in the hope that some people will identify with parts of the lived experiences I am choosing to share with you.

Everyone on the autistic spectrum is *differently autistic,* because the human brain is more diverse than we are able to imagine. We are all products of different environments and experiences and nobody is ALWAYS *anything.* The media likes to portray autism in a certain way, but there are many 'autistic traits' that I just don't have, and that is normal. Personality comes first and personality can have an impact on how autism outwardly presents itself. For this reason, the *only* way to learn about the condition is to put down the books and communicate with *your* autistic people directly.

It is nice to meet you. My name is Claire.

I have a big, wonderful family. I have passion, motivation and extraordinary friendships. I am musical and I am in a choir called *Sing Now Choir* (which is directed by my best friend Jack, who you will hear about a lot throughout this book.) I am reliable. I am empathetic. I adore my job as a primary school teacher. I have love, courage and Autism Spectrum Disorder. I love creative projects, choreography, caring for children and the elderly, Disney, musical theatre, animals, flowers, cosy-warm things … and I carry around the isolating feeling that, wherever I go, I am *the alien in the room.*

**Claire Murphy**

# What on Earth is Autism?

I have heard many autistic people say that they find this question impossible to answer. Asking an autistic person what autism is, or what it's like to be autistic, is like asking someone without autism what it's like to *not* be autistic.

Where do you start?

Over time, and given the right support, you can begin to understand autism as you experience it, but autistic people grow and change with age and differing circumstances just as everybody does.

For this reason it is often easier to talk about what autism *isn't*.

Autism is as varied as the people that 'have' it, therefore it is not restricted to socially awkward *boys,* obsessed with dinosaurs, trains and Lego. Girls can be autistic too, even girls that wear make-up, have children of their own and enjoy going to parties.

Autism *isn't* a learning disability or a mental health disorder - neither do we all have Savant syndrome or 'super powers.' It should *not* affect employability as much as it does. I may think and communicate differently but this has no impact on my intelligence.

Not everyone is somewhere 'on the spectrum,' and autism is *not* a linear continuum labelled mild-to-severe on which you can plot your whole self. *High-functioning* and *low-functioning* are not helpful labels for anyone, with any condition. They spark assumptions that high-functioning autism is 'mild,' and requires less support, and that low-functioning autism is 'severe,' but autism impacts every single adult and child differently. It is completely incomparable. My autism has always been carefully hidden, so much so that even I didn't know it was there until I turned 30. It may have a mild effect on the people around me, but nobody can see how severely it is affecting me, because I 'mask' to fit in.

Autism is lifelong and nobody grows out of it when they reach adulthood. It is not an illness and it cannot be cured. However, if ignored, undetected or misdiagnosed as something else, it can lead to mental illness and suicide, especially when autistic people try to hide their differences. We can feel like a social 'problem'. This is not because of autism directly, but because our brains do not fit with the society that is everyone else calls 'normal' and this can lead to misunderstanding, bullying and/or isolation.

Autism is an explanation, not an excuse. We should never use a diagnosis to 'opt out' of society but should find different ways to navigate socially and to be successful. *Everything is differently accessible*, and, any progress autistic adults make regarding social acceptance creates a smoother pathway for the autistic children growing up behind us.

*Autism is one word, trying to describe zillions of different stories.*

But before I introduce you to my autism …

Let me introduce you to my cat …

Saffie-Cat and I moved house recently.

We didn't *want* to move house. We liked the house we rented in Bluebell Road, but we needed to move in with my parents for a little while because of autism. The reasons for this will become clear later.

Saffie was born on the first anniversary of my Gran's death to my cousin Sophie's cat, Poppy. She is my support-animal and she has brought joy to my life without knowing it. *How special to bring joy without knowing it.* She is comforting and consistent. Her fur is silky-smooth, black and soothing to touch. When she sleeps on my tummy, the weight of her relaxes me and somehow reminds me that I am *real*. When I look into her amber eyes, I feel loved, because I am the only one she will make eye-contact with for any stretch of time, and vice-versa.

*But it wasn't until we moved that I thought she might be autistic.*

The change disturbed her.

She spent three days squashed down the side of the bed, against the wall, wide-eyed. I don't know how she managed to get down there because the space was so small, and her little scared eyes would stare up at me and break my heart.

Gradually, Saffie ventured out and began to explore in her own time. I tried to make our bedroom look and smell the same as my bedroom at our old house, so that she could feel 'right.' We like fresh-blossom room-scents and dim mood-lighting. We like the feel of a certain brushed-cotton duvet cover and blanket, and the aura and simplicity of gentle, quiet colours.

We need things to stay the same.

Most people do. Most people feel safe in this changeable world when things stay the same, even those without social, mental and sensory variances. Sameness, for Saffie and me, is crucial to our ability to function, for so many reasons.

For the first two nights, Saffie didn't eat or sleep. Changes upset my senses, my feelings and my tummy. They upset my mind and my ability to achieve the most ordinary daily things. When something changes, it is hard to remember that not *everything* has changed. It is hard to remember that my friends still like me, my interests are still my interests, my thoughts, behaviour, beliefs are all still the same. I still have the same doctor's appointment booked and the same book I'm halfway through reading. But when you have autism, it is hard to remember all of this.

Slowly, Saffie remembered that she likes to eat chicken-in-gravy at five o'clock in the afternoon, and likes to fall asleep in the corners I make with my bent legs when I sleep on my side. She remembered that she likes watching TV, chasing ribbons and drinking water

... looking
out into
a world
that she
will never,
truly,
understand
...

from the taps. She remembered that she doesn't like being picked up, but does like to always be close by and she loves a cuddle (on her terms.) She remembered that she doesn't eat anything unless it is put in her cream-coloured bowl. She doesn't like having her claws clipped but she *does* like waking me up at four o'clock on the dot every morning by licking my eyes and pawing my face.

Saffie stayed in my bedroom for about a week before she was bold enough to meet the other cats in the house, Merlin and Mollie.

Although Saffie is a loving cat, interactions with others can sometimes be traumatic. Being around others that *look* like you but don't *think* like you can highlight your cognitive differences and cause anxiety, misunderstanding, and a decreased sense of worth. This is how I feel about myself when I am among other adults. Saffie wanted to be friends with Merlin but he ran away from her because he is a cool cat who associates with 'street-wise' cats. He doesn't understand her and he doesn't want to. So she tried to make friends with Mollie by licking her, which was apparently not socially acceptable, because Mollie responded with a hiss and a growl.

*Saffie ran back up to my bedroom to be by herself instead.*

She has never really known how to make friends, so the older she gets, the more isolated she feels.

She used to have a friend at our old house called Dobby. He was easier for her to get along with because he was a boy cat and he was older. For some reason, she gets on better with boys. Dobby was also a creature of habit, stuck in his patterns. She would follow him, copy him and learn from him. She learned to be herself around him, the way I can be myself around my friend Jack, who I have known for ten years. Moving away from Dobby has been another difficult change for Saffie to adapt to.

She needs space and time and plenty of silence to 'recharge her batteries' … as they say.

Noise triggers Saffie's 'catxiety' and she cannot concentrate or function when there are new or loud noises, or too many noises all at once. I am sympathetic when she is distressed by noise because she cannot put her paws over her ears to block it out like I can. Her other senses are heightened too, such as touch and smell, but some things that bother other cats don't bother her at all, like dogs and danger.

She doesn't like weather, though.

Weather sometimes causes us uncomfortable sensory feelings or forces us to change our plans. We don't like the snowy weather, but thunder and lightning is worse. It is loud, unexpected, and you can't control it. It is full of suspense, like a mannequin, or dead shark eyes that make you feel like something terrible is going to happen in slow motion.

I sometimes see Saffie looking out of the window at the weather like an outsider looking out into a world she will never truly understand.

Especially on firework nights.

Sometimes, when things get really overwhelming, she goes wild and darts around like a caged bat, chasing imaginary things and shadows as if to release the discomfort that has built inside her. She climbs curtains and knocks things over. Sometimes she sits and kneads my jumper or blanket, as if she is stimming - pushing the anxiety out of her body through her paws.

After three weeks, Saffie went outside into my parents' garden for the very first time.

As her little paws touched the concrete she paused: it felt … new. A piece of fluff flew about her face like a fly and she chased it with her eyes. Confidence grew as she walked through the grass, stopping every so often to glance back at me. A pigeon clapped its wings overhead and she cowered, then ran toward a tree: she clawed the bark and rubbed her face against the trunk. After twenty minutes and a brain full of new sensory stimulation, she pranced back into the house and up the stairs to our bedroom, our sanctuary.

That was enough.

She slept there for four hours, overawed and exhausted by the things she had touched, smelt, heard, tasted and seen all in one go. She was probably over-thinking her interactions with the other cats too. I say 'probably' because, of course, Saffie doesn't communicate her emotions. I can tell when she is sad because she goes off her food, or she hides. When she is happy she slowly blinks as she purrs, or falls asleep across my neck like a silky black scarf. It is hard to know about other feelings apart from simply 'positive' or 'negative.' I can sometimes tell by the size of her pupils, but her expression never seems to change.

Saffie is safe and solitary.

There is no doubt that she likes me and my company, and she communicates this to me without words. I know her. Once I even bought a black-cat dressing-up costume to wear to a choir Christmas 'social' so that I could *be* her.

*I didn't know how to go to the party as myself.*

# Autism is a Curse

Autism is a curse on the worst days.

Autism is being the only teacher on playground duty, in the depth of winter, with no coat and gloves. It is finally buying a coat, not because it's cold, but to try and prove to other adults that I have a coat, an organised mind and a body that experiences temperature the same as everyone else. Autism is the discomfort of a washed sock touching my toenails, a toothbrush on my teeth, or the texture of cauliflower cheese in my mouth. It's the addiction to a certain jumper that I can't *not* wear (even if it is hot, or socially odd) because it makes the whole day more tolerable. It's 'not knowing' all the things other people 'just know'. It's having a different 'common sense' with regard to communication, which is less 'common,' and much more sensible.

Autism is a social disability. It is OK to call it that, because it is disabling. It is being an 'alien' in your own skin. It is the subsequent and constant fear of humiliation and loneliness.

Autism is not being easily able to transform thoughts into words. It is not being able to identify and share feelings. It won't process grief or change effectively. It is cancelling a London trip to see your favourite theatre show, because one change of plan makes your entire world come crashing down. Autism communicates honesty inappropriately but does not understand why. It looks rude, angry, and awkward when really it's eager to please. It is the frustrating inability to comprehend and participate in 'small-talk,' falseness and niceties.

Autism is misunderstandings.

It is confusion.

It is electricity in my brain that speeds everything up when someone talks to me unexpectedly. It is knowing what to say but not being able to say it in the right order. It is frustration. It is paranoia. It is copying what someone just said, to 'mask' verbal inadequacy. Autism hyper-focusses on one subject to talk about, like the state capitals of America, or *The Chase*, or *Wicked* the musical, or Saffie-Cat, repetitively. It is obsessive and boring to the people around me, but it's hard to stop. It is reassuring to know that I do *know* things, and I use my interests to drown out the rest of the unpredictable world.

Autism is feeling left out and not knowing how to join in. It is being easily manipulated, easily taken advantage of. Tricked. It is always being 'on the back foot' in any social gathering or friendship group. It is being forgotten, replaced, ignored, excluded and overlooked.

Invisible.

It is being talked-over, talked-down, down-trodden.

Autism is the world, amplified. It is the inability to filter out 'unnecessary' sensory information, particularly in times of stress. It is over-stimulation. Meltdowns. Shutdowns. It is a condition in which noise makes me sick with pain and flashing lights make me over-heat. It is never quite finding silence. Autism is certain sounds or words that itch and burn my inner ears, and certain fabrics that itch and burn my skin, even after I have removed them. It is a fear, not a dislike, of 'everyday things' that my brain is not equipped to manage or tolerate, like air-conditioning, hand dryers, overlapping conversations, weather, fireworks, doctor's appointments, banks, social media, public transport, people, chores, pantomimes … but it obstinately tries to manage and tolerate them.

Autism is rigid rules and routine.

Autism is only being confident to do what I am told, taught or shown.

Autism is wanting things to be so frantically perfect that I end up spoiling them, like friendships, relationships, jobs. Autism can be self-conscious. It does not know when to stop. It is like being an adult in a foreign country where you don't speak the language. Autism is often disguised by a desire to mimic 'normality' and is thus accompanied by failure, burnout and clinical anxiety. It is definitely failure. It can't manage finances or go to the optician or the shops without dread. It is the choice between forcing myself into uncomfortable situations to 'fit in' or facing social isolation and depression because I don't. It is a pendulum that swings from social competence to social incompetence and exhaustion in the space of a sentence. It stims to regulate the unfathomable world of human emotion and inconsistency.

It's living inside a body that doesn't necessarily fit me.

It is longing to swap brains with my best friends for just a minute, so that they can experience the world the way I do, and I can see the world through their eyes too, having spent thirty-one years with the belief that the world is the same for me as it is for everyone else.

It is sleepless nights, seizures, self-doubt, guilt, social isolation, self-hatred and suicidal ideation.

*Autism is a curse on the worst days.*

I cannot speak.
For whatever reason, God intended me to be mute.
Many people believe that I cannot think,
but despite their thinking, I can.
What's more is that I listen.


Neal Katz,
A nineteen-year-old non-verbal autistic teenager from Los Angeles.

# A Constellation of Stars

Autism is not a learning disability but people still think it is.

Autism has no negative impact on my *intelligence*, but it does affect how I *communicate* my intelligence because it is a social and communication (dif)ability. Autistic people are often academically able but socialise and communicate differently, perhaps becoming isolated from their peers and from other people who cannot understand their ways and values.

Sometimes autistic people have *additional* learning disabilities, but this isn't autism.

Autistic people often have 'co-morbid conditions' – in other words, long-term conditions that exist alongside their autism – such as sensory processing disorder (which affects the way in which the brain receives and responds to information from the senses), alexithymia (the inability to identify emotions), epilepsy, dyspraxia (which affects motor coordination), mental health problems, gastrointestinal problems and many others. I don't know why because I'm not an expert, but these 'co-morbid conditions' are not exclusive to, or *part* of Autism, they just 'hold hands' with it sometimes and create confusion.

The Autism Spectrum is not a linear continuum that goes from mild-to-severe, and not everyone is 'on the spectrum somewhere'. Those are myths that cause misunderstandings about autism. They cause 'actually-autistic' people to feel muted, invalidated and alone. There are *many* different spectrums within autism. Each autistic characteristic has its *own* spectrum of severity. Each spectrum can be triggered or soothed by different environments, people, senses and circumstances. Everyone with an autism diagnosis will experience the condition severely at times, and mildly at others.

It changes all the time depending on many things, just like the ever-changing minds of people without autism.

I have imagined the autism spectrum as being a three-dimensional *constellation of stars*, interlinking, inside an autistic brain. The biggest stars are the main characteristics: social differences, communication differences, repetitive behaviours, executive function difficulties, and sensory differences including anxiety.

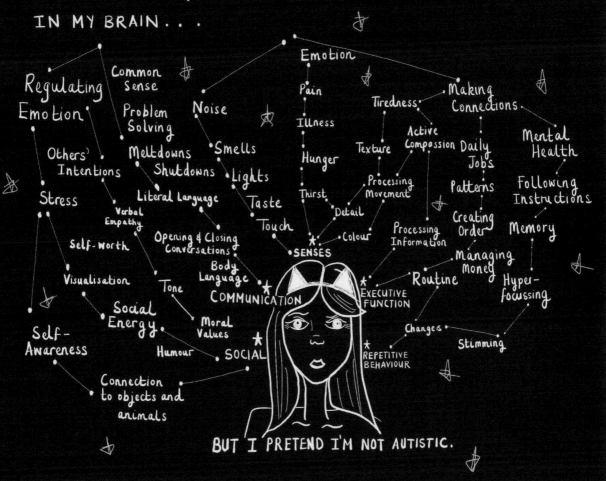

ALL THESE THINGS BEHAVE DIFFERENTLY
IN MY BRAIN . . .

BUT I PRETEND I'M NOT AUTISTIC.

Each of the main stars is surrounded by thousands of smaller stars that link to it. The smaller stars can sometimes represent the outward behaviours adopted by the autistic person to *manage* the world.

These smaller stars are not always 'symptoms' of autism, but common human traits or signs that many anxious people share. We all find aspects of life differently tolerable. We all develop behaviours and soothing mechanisms to manage and control things: we are all human, but we do not all have an autistic brain.

The National Autistic Society tells us that autism is "*a lifelong, neuro-developmental disorder that affects how a person communicates with, and relates to, other people, and how they experience the world around them.*" This definition gives you the space to explore how autism manifests itself for you, or your friend, relative, pupil or colleague.

My autism assessment report covers twelve pages of A4 paper and I felt I could have done with a degree in psychology to understand it. It tells me that I present with Autism Spectrum Disorder. It would have previously been called Asperger's Syndrome, under earlier diagnostic criteria. In reality I am *mostly* 'high-functioning', *sometimes* 'low-functioning'. Some days, due to varying circumstances, I am not functioning *at all*, but these functioning labels say more about how the people around me experience my autism, rather than how I experience it myself.

The report tells me that I display "functional limitations in social communication, social participation and social relationships." It tells me that the impacts of my difficulties with social-emotional engagement are "significant." It tells me that I have "clear difficulties in relation to engaging in 'unusual behaviours, communicating verbally with adults especially groups of adults, tolerating changes and sensory stimulation." I have "highly restricted, fixated interests that are abnormal in intensity." I experience "extreme distress at small changes, difficulties with transitions, hyper and hypo-reactivity to sensory input, apparent indifference to pain/temperature, repetitive motor movements and abnormalities in eye-contact and body language."

But what on earth does this *mean*?

I think it means I experience the whole world differently, because my whole brain is different to the non-autistic brain. Some people strive for difference, and diversity within the 'realm of normality' is accepted, encouraged and 'cool'… but autism currently exists *outside* of society's 'realm of normality', which is not 'cool' at all. Often – due to my differences – my experience of the world is terrifying. To regulate the fear, I lose myself in solitude, in the safety of my interests, in facts and creative projects. I abide by strict routines and consciously create order in everything I do to reduce the anxiety of 'being *too* different.' I spend most of my time pretending that I am not autistic. I make rigid plans and I engage (consciously or subconsciously) in repetitive behaviours, in an effort to regulate unidentifiable emotion, social and communication differences, difficult sensory input, and change. But these visible 'traits' of my autism are just the tip of the iceberg compared to what happens constantly inside my brain.

*You don't look autistic…* is what people say.

The more effort I put in to creating visual order, the more distressing it is when things feel out of control, when plans change, or when there is uncertainty about a plan.

When a change of plan happens, I withdraw because I lack the ability to adapt without physical anxiety. I use a lot of energy trying to disguise this anxiety, and I have learned to distract others from being able to recognise it. This is because I want to be loved and included, and I want to be able to form friendships and relationships like everyone else. Not being naturally able to win respect, affection and friendship makes me question myself and my place in the world. Not being able to *be myself* means that the relationships I *do* make, don't last. But despite the negativity of the language of my assessment report (which used words like limitations, difficulties, unusual, abnormal) I know – from working with autistic children as a teacher – that there are many positives to having an autistic mind.

I just have to find out what they are …

So why get a diagnosis?

A lifetime of 'not knowing why' plunged me into depression and I became suicidal.

After initial shock and shame, it was a *relief* to be diagnosed with autism. A diagnosis doesn't change me, or magic away my difficulties. It gives me a 'new pair of glasses' through which I can see *my* world more clearly and more compassionately. Hopefully the people around me can acknowledge the diagnosis too.

A diagnosis gives me permission to give myself a break, to make sense of the past. It enables me to get the specific support I need in order to keep going. It allows me to make sense of the behaviours and the life that is mine and own it, *improve it accordingly,* instead of wanting to hide it … and end it. It gives me the opportunity to reach out to *people like me* in groups and on social media. People I can finally relate to. It gives the people around me an opportunity to understand, which enables longer-lasting relationships and it gives me the opportunity to share my experience in the hope of helping others.

Things are 'adding-up' since my diagnosis day. For the first time, I am starting to accept traits, strengths and difficulties to which I have never given time, thought and value before.

Thank you for being here with me.

*Let's explore some more.*

# Ten Bright Stars

Every autistic person has millions of spectrums of stars in their mind, shining differently. Let me share ten of mine.

**1** I have lived my whole life not knowing my own feelings. I can now identify and accept a scale of basic feelings that I have connected to numbers in my head in order to respond to them healthily. I have learned that I am not sure when I feel tired, which explains why I never know when to stop. This also links to my sensory differences and the disconnection between my mind and the senses within my body.

**2** Despite traumas I have experienced, I did not grieve conventionally. The combination of shock and autism transformed me into a mechanical robot that hyper-focussed on rigid and familiar rituals and routines in order to escape and ignore the uncomfortable emotions of grief, change, loss and pain. This 'skill' made me ill because I am actually (believe it or not) a human being, so I am working on everything constructively now and doing very well.

**3** My brain does not filter out 'irrelevant' senses, such as background noise, the feel of clothes on my skin, intricate detail, or people moving around. This means I have to process everything at once, which affects my ability to communicate and identify abstract feelings. My assessment revealed '*clinical concern for sensory overload*.' When overload happens I am hot, sick and overwhelmed and it triggers an intense meltdown or a shutdown reaction that is not always obvious to others.

**4** I have verbal and physical stimming behaviours that are subconscious like rocking, humming, and rubbing or banging my wrists together. Autistic stims are more noticeable, sometimes more harmful and less socially acceptable than 'normal habits.' Many autistic people stim in excitement, in order to process their thoughts, in order to calm down stressful situations, or in an effort to quieten a difficult sense with a soothing one. It can feel like relief, and is a healthy way of regulating emotions. I do my best to suppress my stims if I am *aware*, because I have learned that it is a bit socially odd. This puts me under emotional pressure and explains why my body aches a lot sometimes.

**5** I *can* make eye-contact but I do not enjoy it. It is difficult for me to concentrate on what someone is saying if I have to look them in the eye (unless I know them really well) because auditory *and* visual social input is hard to process simultaneously, as are many other sensory combinations.

**6** When people talk to me unexpectedly, I panic. This is because I do not understand the unwritten rules and intentions of small-talk. I am literal and matter-of-fact, which puts some people off me. I plan conversations in advance and predict possible outcomes. I over-think and I am sometimes introverted. I worry that I will say something insensitive, unacceptably honest or weird without knowing it, if there is too much freedom in the conversation, and I share these traits with socially anxious people. Sometimes, depending on the light and sound in my environment, it takes me a long time to process auditory information and then work out my response. I like conversations to have a clear purpose, a clear beginning and a clear ending.

**7** I have started to realise some *good* things about my autism already. I have a great memory. I love analysing data, memorising numbers, intricate details, patterns, lists, facts, song lyrics, solving problems, links, words, being creative, studying human behaviour and finding *answers* and I have a superbly long attention span for these things. I am very reliable and thorough. I do things quicker and better than people expect them to be done, if I fully understand the job, because of my ability to focus, and I am painfully intuitive to *others'* feelings.

**8** I imitate girls my age so I know how to behave in new situations. It's a bit like being a copycat, or a chameleon blending in. I am *seriously* good at it. Since my diagnosis I have felt less pressure to do this consciously. Sometimes I repeat what people say when *I* don't know what to say, to avoid an awkward silence and to help me process what is being said; it's like a verbal 'stim'. I realise that I am not often friends with girls my age because I feel very different to them, and it highlights my deficits to be near them. I do like them, though. I have learned to 'mask' (what I now know to be) my autism, because I want to fit in, but *still* there is a natural barrier between me and other people.

**9** I am *constantly* preoccupied with 'right' and 'wrong,' 'good' and 'bad.' It *never* stops. I think this is why 'grey areas' cause me such unease. My brain is black-and-white, this-or-that. This can be wrongly received as a lack of empathy, which makes relationships difficult, but this is frustrating because I am in fact an empath with a strong sense of social justice and morals, and the ability to solve problems that other people cannot find solutions to. I am fascinated by religion, law, education, care, crime and the police. Social media and the news are confusing and induce periods of anxiety, but, in general, I am very interested in, and protective of, people.

**10** It is *impossible* to deal with a change of plan. For this reason, and social/sensory reasons combined, it is hard to socialise with more than one or two people at a time. The more people there are, the more complicated things become, especially if I know them all well. Sudden unexpected changes and unpredictable overlapping conversations force me into sensory, information or emotional 'overload', which may or may not be noticeable to others. Either way, the aftermath of any overload is physically and mentally exhausting for a couple of days.

# Knowing What to Do and When to Stop

Imagine again, that the Autism Spectrum is a three-dimensional constellation of stars.

Imagine that each cluster of stars represents a *part* of Autism, and that *all* of those stars are connected inside the brain of somebody who is autistic.

Executive functioning is one cluster in my spectrum. It is something I am bad at when I am anxious, overwhelmed or hyper-focussed, but *obsessively* good at the rest of the time. It is an admission that I never dreamed I would share for shame. It is something that I still do not fully understand. Following diagnosis, I am happier to admit and acknowledge it now that I know, to my relief, that it is part of the condition I have and nothing to do with laziness, disorganisation or a lack of intelligence.

Autistic speaker Ros Blackburn helped me to understand my brain better by simplifying it like this:

*"I can only do things I am told, taught or shown."*

Executive function refers to all the thinking skills that help me cope in my daily life and get things done. It is the ability to make a connection, a decision, change a plan, multi-task, *stop* a task, regulate emotion, filter out unnecessary sensory information, be socially spontaneous, remember a *full* set of instructions, carry out a task in order, and create a sensible 'balance'. It is all of the things people generally 'just do' without having to be explicitly taught. These commonsense skills do not come naturally to all autistic people and are rarely taught in schools.

Having phases of poor executive function is a bit like being an Alexa robot. You respond well to direction and can carry out clear instructions with speed and precision in the right circumstances, but without those instructions you don't really function much at all.

It was one of the indicators that first pointed towards autism in me.

I was thriving at work, having been promoted. I would finish my jobs and then do someone else's. I was obsessed with progression. I was fast and thorough. Confident. I was obsessed with intricate marking, data analysis, grades, inspiring planning, inventing new

# EXECUTIVE FUNCTION
## How my brain works...

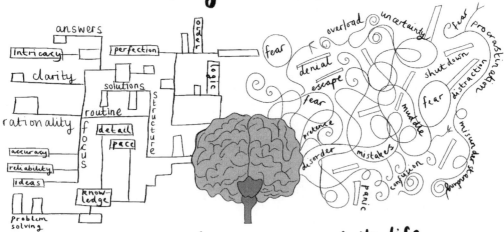

... when people need me
... at work
... special interests
... creative projects

... daily life
... every day jobs
... appointments
... social events and communication.

initiatives, delivering the best lessons ever, aiming for *beyond* outstanding. I was teaching other teachers how to teach, leading meetings, training. Addicted to making everyone's lives easier … and frightened of letting anybody down. I was entirely motivated, entirely focussed, but the 'drive' and 'threat' systems in my brain were spurring each other on, and that became my 'normal'.

I had no comforts but alcohol, which comes with its own set of problems.

I was giving my brain work-related instructions constantly because work made sense to me, but the rest of daily living did not.

Consequently, in the weeks building up to my thirty-first birthday I ate nothing. I drank a bottle of wine every night whilst working in the one-bedroomed flat I lived in at that time, because, along with my work, it helped to block my own life out. The heating was broken and, with no double-glazing, I was freezing cold. All the light-bulbs needed replacing. I hadn't slept in my bed for months, choosing to work on the sofa by candlelight (where I would accidentally occasionally fall asleep.) I spent a lot of time checking the flat, alert to every sound, scared of fires, burglars and tiny muffled creaks. I acquired (and ignored) six parking tickets, because somebody else was parking in my allocated space and I didn't have the social competency to challenge it.

My life, on the outside, looked perfect, and to my knowledge it was no different to anyone else's.

But everything crashed on my thirty-first birthday.

I could not even cope with the thought of my best friend Jack coming into my flat after my party, but he insisted.

Neither he, nor anybody, had been allowed inside my flat for months.

To the left was the bathroom, the cleanest room in the flat, save for the dogged mould coming in from the roof-hatch and developing beneath the laminate flooring. Straight ahead, my bedroom door remained firmly shut, as it had been for weeks. We walked into the lounge. A chill licked our legs and there was dampness.

It was desperately cold.

I looked around as if seeing it all for the first time, through Jack's eyes.

The sofa, where I had been sleeping and working for the past seven months, was covered in blankets, a perfumed pillow and a king-sized brushed-cotton winter duvet. My hot water bottle was there, waiting to be filled, and Jack went to the kitchen to fill it up. My heart sank as he neared the sink. He didn't flinch when he saw the pile of neglected washing-up, the tea-stained worktops or the collection of empty wine bottles that had filled a whole cupboard, and were now overflowing onto the floor and the preparation space beside the sink.

I feel dangerously safe in my skin when I have a glass of wine in my hand. Heaven knows what he must have been thinking about me.

*Don't tell anyone, Jack.*

I was struggling to understand the abstract concept of money. My car needed fixing and it had been clamped because it wasn't taxed. I had lost contact with nearly *all* of my friends. I had a list of jobs to sort out with the bank. I didn't know how to get repeat prescriptions. Things that were not related to work, or things that required human interaction, communication or prioritising myself, couldn't be processed. I had to fight my own *brain* to do simple tasks like opening the curtains, eating, washing my clothes, and answering a text. I hadn't the flexibility in my mind to deal with unexpected traffic, weather or phone-calls.

I beat myself up in the mirror.

*You are a lazy, useless, broken, odd, selfish, difficult, lonely, disconnected, fake, burdensome accident.*

I didn't know then, that I am a*utistic*.

I know now that I used work as an escape from the uncertainty of daily life and that my brain was failing to make the connections other people 'just make' in order to get ordinary things done. I had no mindfulness skills and had developed the firm belief that I was undeserving of comfort, and intrinsically 'bad'. I worked through hunger, thirst, tiredness, illness and pain because my body doesn't identify those sensations easily, and my mind prioritised my work over myself. I respond gratefully and directly to instructions. Instructions give me certainty that I am doing the 'right thing,' and I am anxious to please, fuelled by a self-conscious awareness of my differences and a desire to be seen as 'good' and 'reliable' to hide the 'bad' inside.

My inflexible brain hyper-focusses on interests like teaching and learning to the extent that everything else gets shut out. It doesn't know when to stop. It *won't* stop. It doesn't identify and respond to emotion. My day needs to be carefully planned from start-to-finish so that *ordinary* things get remembered during the difficult times. Any 'extras' or tiny little changes cause fear, which trigger compulsions or cannot be processed at all. The state of my flat was due to a combination of complicated things that I could never have understood before my diagnosis of autism.

I have changed my living circumstances now - luckily my incredible parents had space for me to move in and recuperate – and I am training my brain with a wonderful therapist, and putting things in place so that this will never happen again.

"*Try and get some sleep,*" Jack said, "*and I'll watch over the flat tonight.*"

I will never *not* be autistic. But with support I am learning that clear instructions, visual routines and plans are helpful for me.

> *I need reminders that I am a human*
> *not a machine*

There are many things that I have learned to instruct *myself* to do, for the hours, days and weeks ahead, now that I have answers and routines to embed. Autism is the *explanation*, but it is not an *excuse*. There is nothing I *can't* do, but I am doing a good job in therapy of learning my limits and figuring it all out step-by-step so that I can succeed intellectually *and* socially and then share my knowledge with people that might need it.

That is my very limited understanding of executive functioning.

*Alexa, dim the lights.*

# Fifty Things People 'Just Do'

1. Understand and use sarcasm
2. Make friends
3. Move from an 'acquaintanceship' to a 'friendship' with someone
4. Start a conversation
5. End a conversation
6. Initiate hugs
7. Use facial expressions that match feelings
8. Name feelings, share them, respond accordingly to them
9. Go to parties
10. Use public toilets
11. Think out loud
12. Read between the lines
13. Prioritise
14. Stop a job before it is fully completed
15. Pay attention to self-care
16. Make eye-contact
17. Understand 'grey areas'
18. Change the plan
19. Change their mind
20. Say 'no' to unrealistic requests
21. Know their limits
22. Understand negative body language in others (sad, angry, disappointed, tired)
23. Know what is 'too little,' and what is 'too much'
24. Book appointments and attend them
25. Send emails without ruminating over them

26. Text how they talk
27. Show empathy with spoken words and expressions
28. Lie or 'cloak the truth'
29. Go 'with the flow'
30. Grieve
31. Fall in love
32. Budget
33. 'Get' jokes
34. Pay bills
35. Adapt appropriately to a change of temperature
36. Plan meals
37. Walk 'on eggshells'
38. Handle finances
39. Plan day-to-day
40. Go shopping
41. Keep in touch
42. Keep up with chores in a balanced way (neither neglecting nor obsessing)
43. Relax
44. Make phone calls and send text messages
45. Manage alcohol and clothes
46. Filter out irrelevant senses
47. Communicate in a group
48. Think 'on their feet'
49. Process spoken information/instructions quickly
50. Know when they are welcome/ not welcome

# My Alien Brain

Autism is complex and really hard to explain, which is why there are so many misconceptions caused by non-autistic professionals who have tried to simplify it. As humans we are not really designed to fully understand *any* mind.

Alexa the robot won't do anything if she is not instructed.

She won't wash the dishes, or pay the bills, or make a phone call when she has a spare five minutes. She won't sing a song, put the radio on, or look something up on the internet, because she lacks social imagination. She will just sit silently on the shelf, and wait for her next instruction. When she is given the instruction, she will perform it with confidence, pace and perfection. Alexa isn't lazy or unintelligent. She cannot think what the logical order might be to do everyday things on her own because she is not programmed to. She cannot envisage another person doing it. She sometimes cannot envisage the end result, or, if she can envisage it, she finds it hard to process the steps that must be taken to achieve it.

When you have autism, each tiny job has its own set of instructions and details that come before it, and this is overwhelming. Every detail needs to make sense. This makes it practically impossible to 'just get on with it' like everyone else does because not many things in the social world 'make sense.' You might observe that something needs doing, but you don't respond to it the way non-autistic people do. Things build up … and you get knocks on your door from bailiffs. The neighbours are complaining about the state of your garden. Your car is uninsured. Your ceiling is falling in. You've run out of clean bedding. Your freezer is empty and you cannot do a thing about it. This is one reason why many autistic people need an official diagnosis and support. Yet we can function so rationally in the right work environments, in emergencies, when there are social problems to be fixed or when someone else needs help. Whilst, for most people, the emotions in emergency situations run high, the solutions *make sense* and are normally simple (such as phone the ambulance, stop the bleeding, combat climate change etc). It is easy for us to see solutions to bigger problems that others can overcomplicate.

In the life gaps and empty spaces in which there are no daily rules, routines or instructions, there is only *anxiety* and the strange, alien, uncertain sense of floating. In these moments we all turn to whatever can give us comfort and keep us grounded, because anxiety is a debilitating experience for everyone. It is dangerous. It spirals out of control quickly. My comforts include helping other people live their lives, or losing myself in creative projects and interests. My interests, including teaching, divert my attention away from the fact that I do not know how to *be* in the world when there is no direction.

*I don't ask for help.*

*I don't know how, when, or that I even need help.*

*I don't know if 'help' will be too unpredictable and make things worse.*

I rely on plans, routines and rituals in order to function, and I can be relied upon to do these things without fail and to an exceptionally high standard when they are embedded, which is why I, and other autistic people, are valuable employees in the right environments. The problem, though, is that these functioning skills don't always translate to every aspect of life. Learning a skill in one environment does not mean I can necessarily do that same skill in a different environment.

I seem to have to learn it all over again.

This is the real and confusing nature of autism.

Just because it's raining doesn't mean I put a waterproof coat on to keep myself warm and dry.

My brain doesn't make connections in the same way as other brains, and my senses behave differently.

Just because the sun is scorching doesn't mean I wind down the car windows or switch on the air-conditioning. Just because the music is too loud, doesn't mean I ask (social skill) to have it turned down. Just because I haven't had a drink since last week doesn't mean I feel thirsty, or think to have a drink *now*. Just because I am hurt doesn't mean I stop, or take painkillers. My tights are itchy and restrictive but I don't take them off – my brain is simply filled by the thought that they are itchy and restrictive – and just because I am in an environment where the sensory stimulation is too much does not mean I leave.

Rather, I am like a hedgehog.

I curl up into a ball in my mind and endure the sensations.

My brain is either failing to *feel* physical and emotional senses, or furiously feeling sensations and making observations, but failing to make the *connections* other people 'just make' in *response* to those observations. When I do make the right connections, I hide my distress if others seem not to be affected by the thing that is affecting me. It's not that I don't pay attention to my mind, mood and behaviour; it's that my mind, mood and behaviour seem *disconnected*.

I enjoy the sensory experience of being rained on. The sun scorches through the closed car windows onto my thighs as I drive, red and burnt, but I cannot feel that, or it just feels tickly. Noises cause me so much discomfort that it is enough to remember to breathe, let alone leave. If I haven't planned that I will be ill or hurt, I work through it, keeping to routine at all costs.

Fear intercepts when there is too much sensory input, sudden change or unfamiliarity, before I am able to identify and respond to it with reason and logic. It's as if I am missing a huge gap of time in which most people would adapt. If solutions involve social interaction, then I am more likely to tolerate whatever I'm experiencing, rather than communicate it. It's about choosing the 'lesser of two evils.' This leads to overload. I think most people would say that this is laziness, overreacting, or a lack of common sense, but it is far more complicated than that. By contrast, if *you* were to have a visible crisis, I would be able to see it, simplify it, deal with it and fix it, *without* emotions like anxiety.

My brain is constantly taking in information but, unlike most people's brains, it does not filter out the information that I do not really need. This can be a gift, but it can also lead to problems and even danger. My sensory differences mean that I am very sensitive in some ways, and not sensitive enough in others. I can smell the shampoo you use from across the room, and notice delightful patterns in a wall when others only see bricks, but I cannot sense the feelings I am having inside my own body.

This is a small part of autism that has a big impact on my life.

You can't see it …

… and it is really hard to understand …

… but it is my every day.

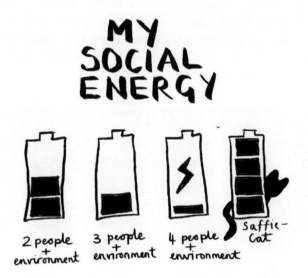

I have a lot to say, and the ability to say it. In a quiet room, with one close friend, I can have deep, illuminating, meaningful, honest, stimulating conversations. With a close friend, in the right environment, I can think, speak, listen, respond, think, speak, listen, and respond. In *public*, or in a group of friends, I can't. My thoughts are filled by my senses. I am worried about the senses I might not be feeling properly. My words don't come out in the order I intend. I cannot filter out all the sensory input in order to focus on what people say to me. I take a long time to process the information I receive, and even longer to find the right response, especially if they are using fillers and phrases that I don't understand, or if there is no clear purpose to the exchange.

I can 'mask' this, and it will be completely unnoticeable to others. Over thirty years of observing people, I have picked up lots of conversational mannerisms that make my disguise authentic, but the more I do this, the more exhausted my brain gets.

Inside I will experience panic.

My thoughts turn to 'overload management.' *How can I participate in this conversation and distract the person from detecting the fact that I am the alien in the room*? I feel heat or electricity in my brain and veins, rising nausea, blurred vision, dizziness and the beating of my heart in my mouth but this is disguised. My first memory of wanting to disguise these feelings was at a family gathering when I was about six years old. A lot of the time I am unaware that I am masking because masking is so ingrained. It is not always clear why the panic comes, and what has caused it, but it is always crushing.

> *My urge to 'shush' people when they talk to me over others, when they talk over background noise or music or a ticking clock, is intense. I cannot understand how they can even find their words amongst all that sound, but they do.*

When someone talks through a film in the cinema, you might 'shush' them so that you can fully concentrate on what is happening in the film. I have learned that in this instance 'shushing' is common and acceptable because everyone wants to focus on one thing: the film. Shushing people in a social gathering when you are not watching a film is rude, even when there are *many things* demanding your whole-hearted attention.

I focus with all my might, read their lips, respond how I think someone else would. This will likely lead me to shame. I might seem awkward, disinterested and distracted, but I am none of these things.

It is hard to make the connection to stop a conversation, and ask if we can talk somewhere quieter, when I'm fighting the urge to just curl up like a hedgehog in the midst of everything.

It is hard to instigate or end *any* conversation when you are autistic, even by text.

A change of environment would need *explanation*. Explaining involves changing the subject, choosing the right words and putting them into ordered sentences *about myself*. Building up to voicing my need for a quieter environment induces anxiety. It will be unrehearsed and impossible to predict how the people in my conversation will react, how they will feel, what they will think of me. It needs attention, and it involves putting my inexplicable needs before others, which doesn't come naturally. By the time the change has happened, the conversation is dead, because I've killed it.

It is hard enough with loved ones and people I know extremely well.

Many autistic people are non-verbal and communicate visually.

This is why I *write*.

# Too Much World

It's like someone said to God … *"Hey God, you made the world TOO good. The humans are never going to be able to cope with all the intricate magic in the world AND communicate with one another AND cope with their daily responsibilities … you need to turn their brains down."*

I experience the world in a different way from neurotypicals. For me, the world is intensified. Touch. Taste. Emotion. Noise. Smells. Lights. Pain. Temperature. Detail. Colour. Movement. The sense of what is happening *inside* the body. Autistic people experience everything much much *more*, and in some cases, much much *less*, making ordinary life much less ordinary. It seems like the sensory wires in our brains have been connected differently to those of other people.

*It sometimes seems like my brain didn't get 'turned down' during the creation process.*

At an early age I learned to mask sensory overload, which is very exhausting.

Since my official autism diagnosis, people have wondered how I manage to cope, as a teacher, with the primary school environment. Teaching isn't for everyone, but it is the most ideal job in the world for me. I follow a very strict timetable at work which rarely ever changes: I don't even need to think about when to take a break, have lunch or go to the bathroom because these break times are scheduled and are the same for everyone, everyday. My classroom is very functional and tidy and I spend a lot of time setting up the environment so that it gives us information but doesn't overwhelm us. It is a familiar space in which I spend the majority of my time, and I know what schools are like having been in them since the age of four. All of my anxiety regarding socialising and communicating disappears when I am with the children: with them I am Miss Murphy the teacher, the professional, the one that knows what's going on. There is no doubt what the expectations are of me at work, there is clear direction and, most importantly, teaching, learning and human behaviour are intense passions and interests of mine. I get to talk, all day, about the

things that I love. Words, numbers, patterns in numbers, religion, diversity, music and finding out how things work, whilst figuring out the behaviour of the children in my class. Fascinating. We explore, discover, create and invent as a team. The children appreciate my need to repeat things and to explain things in detail, they sense my excitement, they feed off it, and they respond when I indicate to them that their noise level is too high. The children *enjoy* that I cannot help but notice their tiny, personal victories, and the expressions on their faces reward me tenfold.

My sensory overload from the classroom is kept inside until I return to my home – the same as it was when I attended school as a child – but there are many circumstances in which the battle of social competency and sensory onslaught is too explosive for my brain to handle. This mainly happens when there is extra anxiety attached to the overload, when I am socialising with adults and navigating unfamiliar environments.

A sensory 'meltdown' is like an anxiety attack caused by *too much world*. It can be an outburst, or sometimes it can be silent. It can stop me from being able to sense my own body's internal signals like fatigue, heat, cold, pain, hunger, thirst, the need to go to the toilet. It can make me physically sick. It can make me shut down like an overwhelmed computer, unable to walk, speak and think. It can cause physical pain. It can make me slur my words, stutter. It can make me hot, disorientated, faint. It can make me depressed. It can make some people hit, cry, scream. This is often labelled 'misbehaviour' in children or 'anti-social' behaviour in adults. But in fact the body is responding exactly as it was *made* to (flight, fight, and freeze) in order to protect itself from perceived danger. The more I mask and work against my body's instinctive, autistic reactions in public, the worse the consequences will be at home, regardless of my passions and 'safe' places.

It has taken 30 years of coping and subconscious covering-up to realise that this is what has been happening to me, all my life.

*How can I not have known?*

It is my thirty-first birthday at the Bellemoor pub in Southampton and I barely have time for it. I have been working non-stop and organising fundraising events for a big dance competition at the Guildhall called the Rock Challenge. I performed in the Rock challenge as a child and want the children I teach to have the opportunity to experience performing on a professional stage to a live audience. I have been hyper-focussed on choreography, lighting design and making costumes for my dancers, but my daily living tasks have all been neglected to the extreme. My best friend Lesley is too ill to come to the pub, last minute. She has warned me lately that perhaps I am doing too much, but I feel energised by my school work and my show preparations.

Someone speaks into a microphone. There's a band playing Beatles songs in the background and many close voices. Close yet indecipherable. Glasses clink together and clunk back onto the table. Laughter. Chair legs scratch the floor and my inner-ear, and the half-open fire-exit door bangs open, closed, open, closed, letting in the freezing January wind.

There is *too much* noise. Noise feels hot. It scalds the edges of my skull.

My pounding heart pumps lava-blood around my body hard and fast. I cannot *breathe*.

Suddenly I am a volcano, building up to a 'meltdown'. Shaking, sweating, faint. Where does 'loud' *start*? Does it start sooner in me than in other people? They seem to *like* the noise, they talk *over* the noise, they make the noise *noisier* and they don't even notice.

● ● ●

I am in the John Lewis department store, about to sing to shoppers with Sing Now Choir.

There are Christmas lights hanging from the roof through the centre of the store, flashing erratically. Stressed shoppers are going up and down the escalators, bustling left and right. There is Christmas music playing. Father Christmas is shaking a bucket of money. Choir members are jostling into lines and crowds are forming. Someone is making a store announcement as Jack asks me to "press play" on the tracks and the background din of the department store is vibrating my brain. I just don't know how the other choir members are coping.

I walk away from the choir.

I am not equipped for the world like the people around me seem to be.

# It Can Help ...

* to visit new environments prior to an event, film the journey, look at photographs of the venue, and study maps of the place we are going to.

* to make detailed plans for outings, know timings, know exactly when it is going to end.

* to be continually reminded about what is going to happen next. If something changes, it is helpful to have the reasons for the change explained in detail so that they make sense.

* to take breaks, and be made to feel like it is OK to take a break in a calm place.

* to feel welcome to use accessible toilets without judgement from others.

* to use noise-cancelling headphones or anything that grounds and comforts us, without judgement from others. Many people have stim toys, sensory aids and soothing items that help regulate difficult senses with more soothing ones.

* if the people around us do not become angry when we struggle. We are not trying to give you a hard time: we are having a hard time and we absolutely dread it.

* to not be expected to communicate verbally when things are difficult.

* if people warn us before they touch us, because unexpected light touches can be painful, whilst deep pressure and weight can relieve anxiety quickly.

* to be given extra time to respond to new verbal, social or sensory information. We sometimes need to juggle a lot of things in order to interact with one thing, and this feels pressured.

* if you give instructions and communicate directly using clear language (i.e. not too many metaphors, analogies, choices or questions.)

* if the people around us know and accept our stimming behaviours if they are safe. (Safe stimming can calm sensory overload, but when the overload is becoming intense the stimming can develop into self-harming behaviour, and at this point it will be necessary for someone to step in and help).

* to stay near to the exit of the venue so that it is easy to leave.

* to have a job or a responsibility to focus on, so that the focus is not solely on anxiety management.

* if the people around us know that a meltdown/shutdown reaction is scary, debilitating and completely involuntary. The aftermath is exhausting on the body and mind and the overriding feeling is shame.

# Hearing

While some autistic people get solace from loud sounds,
I find them to be painful. Especially
when they overlap.

They take away my ability to think and talk.

And breathe.

Others barely notice the sounds that I hear,
each one *overwhelmingly* interesting,
wanting *all* the attention
of my sensitive ears.

Hand dryers,
hair dryers,
air-conditioning
fans and buzzers
distress me beyond explanation,
jumping out-of-my-skin at sudden noises
regardless of volume: an electric sensation.

The pain is spiky-hot,
like my head is burning
and it is hard to discern
how others are *bearing* this burning?

What is it? Where is it coming from?
What causes it to sound this way?

I need to *control* it.
To turn it down, or turn it off, while
others drown it out by making their own noises
over the top.

Due to my zeal to fit in,
I 'mask' in uncomfortable environments
where even *silence* isn't silent.

Noise makes social interaction
even more disjointed
distracted
awkward.

Prolonged noise demands
so much concentration,
that I hold my breath
losing the senses *within* my body
when I try and endure it.

# Vision

Fluorescent lights hurt my head and eyes
because they are *too* bright.
Lights on iPhones,
computer screens,
TV shows
need to be dimmed because
I cannot look at them.

Sunlight,
pulsing lights,
strobe-lighting,
are all painful
and frightening.

Oppressing lights in hospitals,
supermarkets, department stores,
public toilets
and other windowless places
generate hot anxiety and, again
it is hard to understand just how
other people cope.

Bright lights speed my heart up
making noise noisier and faster.
Dim lights slow things down.

Dim lights make communication more achievable
and calm the risk of a *meltdown*.

I wear my sunglasses inside
if the lights are too bright for my eyes,
or if there is too much movement
or too many reflective surfaces.

It's not that I don't *want* to see

It's just *everything* wants to be seen, equally, by me.

# Visualisation

It's impossible to process whole pictures
or whole rooms, visually, in one scan
like non-autistic people can.

Everything I see is a separate piece of puzzle
which my mind *slowly* puts together
to read the situation better.

The world is fragmented,
and hyper-detailed
but focussing on small things
means missing the 'bigger-picture.'

It's being so observant that you see
the pattern on the wing of a butterfly
before you realise that it's a butterfly.
Non-autistic brains work oppositely.
They process and react with more immediacy
but less wonder.

The visual stimulation of supermarket shelves
filled with competing products
puts me under *pressure*.
Interested and overwhelmed
by each feature. Switch on the *sound*
and then even a corner-shop becomes a battleground.

Everything shouting "buy me, buy me, buy me!"

New places and experiences are scary
because there is no prior sensory knowledge.

Experiencing every sense on full-blast
whilst navigating the social protocol
is too much information, and too fast.

Visualisation is a technique used
to reduce 'build-up anxiety' before a *familiar* social event.
But if plans change or things happen differently
it is hard to adapt to it without pronounced anxiety.

I research places, and find photographs online
to help me visualise as much as I can, ahead of time.

# Touch

An unanticipated light touch
from another person, on my skin
makes me prickly, and can be painful depending on
the environment I am in.

Deep pressure is comforting:
a tight hug, a massage,
a weighted blanket
grounds me quickly, so I can
think and breathe more easily.

Some autistic people find it hard to
have their hair cut. The sensation
of loose hair on their skin hurts them.
The bouncing lights in mirrors disconcert them.

The hairdresser's is hard for me because
of hairdryers blasting over the sound of the radio.
The fear of failing at 'small talk'
and being vulnerable.

I am under-sensitive to pain.
This has been dangerous in the past
when I have failed to identify illness and injury
focussing always on completing routines.

I am (sometimes) sensitive to labels in clothes
and certain fabrics on my skin. This changes
depending on what sensory circumstances I am in.

I put on similar, comfortable clothes,
soft pyjamas are my favourite to wear.
I dislike having things in my hair.
I like light make-up on my face
but look forward to taking it off
at night and just being natural.

I have heard that some people on the spectrum
struggle with showering. The water feels
like needles, but I absolutely love it.
Water makes me strong and wonderful
and comforted. I dislike intently
the feel of a toothbrush on my teeth
and old bobbly socks touching my feet.

# Taste, Texture and Hunger

Unlike many autistic people
I'm not a sensitive eater at all.
I avoid slimy foods like rice pudding
but I eat all meats and vegetables.

The texture of food in my mouth is
nowhere near as distressing for me
as for many people with autism spectrum disorder.

It is the sense of hunger that I
always fail to identify.
I regularly forget to eat and drink,
too diverted by other senses, I think.

I never 'crave' or 'fancy'
specific kinds of foods. The idea of
entering a supermarket depletes
my need to eat. I eat
food for survival.

I have never eaten because I am bored
or seen food as some sort of *reward*.
I have never even *experienced* boredom.
Lucky for me, I have alternative
sources of energy.

I dislike eating in front of people
because I feel self-conscious.
But I do enjoy cooking food for friends:
it is an honour. A feeling that I am
in control, and taking care of others, as I should
a worthy sign of adulthood.

# Smell

I am blessed with a super-sense of smell:
it is forensic. Smells are calming and exciting.
I smell things simply by imagining them
in my mind.

Smells help me give feelings meaning.
I seek them when I'm anxious, and can even
smell things when I'm dreaming.

I associate each smell with a temperature or colour.
I am overjoyed when trying to discover
the essences of different smells, and embrace
people by their smell, better than by their face.

I've spent hours, with Lesley, in the Jo Malone store,
testing the perfumes, rescuing
combinations of fragrances from bottles, triumphant.
Wandering around with the perfumed tester-cards for days,
smelling them for comfort.

I enjoy guessing what people have eaten
based on the smells that come from their kitchen.
It's like a game. Spicy or sweet, it fills me up
so that I can exhale contentment.

Smells of bleach,
cleaning products, hair products,
make me energetic.

Scented candles, moisturisers, room sprays,
fruits and flowers are the best.
Many autistic people are distressed
by exposure to too many new smells,

But not me.

They give me utter pleasure and joy.
During times of change,
or environments that are new and strange,
I love to have smells around me.
They reduce the anxiety caused by other senses.

# What's In Your Self-Soothing Kit?

What calms you? What soothes you? I used to think it was selfish and indulgent to pay attention to these soothing mechanisms, but now I realise that every brain has a drive system, a threat system and a soothing system, and that they should all balance out, all of the time, for you to keep well and wise. It isn't selfish, it's science.

It's taken a lifetime for me to grow a 'soothing system'. What would you put in your kit? Here's mine:

## Brain

Noticing my mind traps
  and challenging them.
Adopting a kind perspective.
Mindfulness
Memory games/ quiz

## Smell

Essential oils
Flowers
Perfumes
Scented body lotions
Candles

## Noise

Noise cancelling headphones
Ear plugs
Playlist of my favourite music
Purring cat
Familiar radio programme/podcast/TV box set/film

## Movement/body

Rocking chairs
Rocking
Breathing deeply
Changing my posture
Forcing a smile
Walking outside
Gardening

## Touch/body

Water
Stim toys
Pets
Weighted blanket
Soft things
Hot water bottle
Magnets
Scissors to cut off labels

## Activities

Spending time outside, fresh air, nature, animals, plants
Doing choreography or creative projects
Writing or crafting
Caring for people
Memorising and listing
Finding something that is in a muddle and putting it in order.
Singing while driving

# A Series of Unfortunate Events

Being born on 'the wrong planet' and *not knowing it* has inevitable consequences. In January 2017, after Jack has discovered what my life is like behind closed doors, he drives me to the doctor.

*I am broken, shut down, burnt out. I cannot talk, my legs won't walk, my brain is off. I have been having overwhelming intrusive thoughts about ending my life in different ways, and fighting a battle against them, but now I am too ill to think at all. I can't tell anybody because words fail me, and because of the guilt. Communicating these thoughts is unconceivable. My job is perfect. My home, my life and my mind are all in a mess.*

Doctor Harriot increases the Sertraline – an anti-depressant – that I have been taking and tells me to come back in four weeks.

But Jack drives me back the following morning.

We see the locum. She prescribes Diazepam for anxiety and refers me to the Crisis Team. Crisis Teams care for you if you are having a 'mental emergency' in the community. A different mental health practitioner visits me every other day at home for ten weeks after that, because I am unable to leave the house.

*I hold it in the palm of my hand like it's heavy. I am afraid of taking the Diazapam tablet. Afraid of not being at work. Afraid of what my colleagues think of me. Afraid of letting the children down, afraid of letting my family down. Afraid of being sad because 'sad is bad.' I'm used to being afraid and functioning through it. I am brave in the face of anxiety. Independent. That is how I have always been. I'm not sure what's happened to me.*

Jack hands me my pillow and a glass of water because I am now staying with him. "Take the tablet …" he gently says, "then put your head down." He puts the DVD of *Bridget Jones' Baby* on for me to watch for the eighth time. I follow his instructions because I respond well to direction but I feel like I should be able to look after these things on my own. He reassures me by saying that, if things were the other way around, he knows that I would do the same for him, and this is infinitely true.

I feel muddled by all the different appointment times from the Crisis Team. Every day a different face but the same punishing questions. I have been promised an appointment with

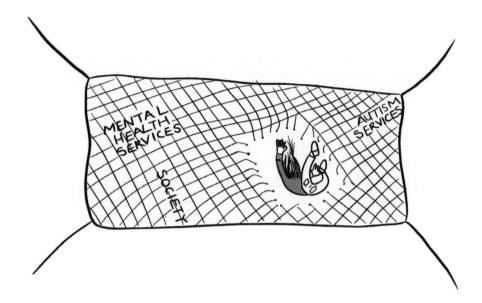

the psychiatrist but unfortunately he is off sick. It's like being on parole: they're just checking I haven't killed myself. No-one is helping me get better and I am dying to be back at work.

In March I am still alive, and I get my appointment with the psychiatrist. He is intelligent and direct. He wants a full psychological history so he interviews me for *hours*, asking straight, emotionless questions that I am able to answer factually and co-operatively. He increases the dosage of Sertraline yet again, and augments that with the anti-psychotic Quetiapine, along with Propanolol for anxiety and Zopiclone to help me sleep. He diagnoses me with depression, anxiety, OCD, an 'unspecified trauma disorder' and potential Autism Spectrum Disorder.

I never see him again.

Each diagnosis feels like a heavy suitcase that I am just supposed to carry around without anyone noticing. No professionals are helping me open up and unpack these suitcases, only Jack is. The more I talk to the 'crisis' team, the more misunderstood I feel. The more I think about it, the more the mental health diagnoses *don't seem to fit*.

A day later a man called Christopher-from-the-Crisis-Team knocks the door.

He looks like Bill Oddie.

He is wearing baggy jeans and an un-ironed shirt that is too small for him. His hands are juggling disorganised paperwork about *me*. He is talking, but I cannot hear him, because my eagle-like senses are exceptionally heightened and circling and merging and all of a sudden, I am Sherlock Holmes. He's a smoker. He just smoked a couple of cigarettes on his way here and is probably thinking of his next one right now. He is also thinking about stopping off at the shop on the way home to collect a bottle of red and a bar of chocolate because he, himself, is depressed, and these are the things he self-medicates with. The circles beneath his eyes cast a shadow on his face that not everyone can see, but I can. I feel sad for him and his sadness, whatever it is. One thing is for sure … he does not want to be here with me. I sit there, battling the chronic sedating side-effects of Quetiapine. Trying and failing to focus and remain awake through the loud cloud of depression. I feel royally sick, lethargic, spaced-out. I want to help Christopher help *me*, but he is not interested in accessing me, I can just tell.

"Are you depressed too?" I ask him.

He doesn't know how to reply.

He ticks a box to say that I am having suicidal thoughts every day.

Jack tells him about my visit to the psychiatrist, and the autism services referral.

*"I knew it was going to be some kind of 'learning dis,"'* …he says.

*I go cold. It is like he has forgotten that he is talking about my life.*

"The waiting list for an autism assessment is *six months* to *two years,*" he says to Jack, as if discussing the delivery time for a pizza rather than putting together a crisis plan. He then transfers me from the Crisis Team to the Community Mental Health Team and cuts my appointment short despite my continuing crisis.

*I don't think they know what to do because of the autism.*

I can hear my friends talking in the hall. They are livid, and it is all my fault.

It takes three whole *weeks* for my notes to be transferred to the Community Mental Health Team.

*When your mind is vulnerable, three minutes is a lifetime.*

In those weeks, with no professional support and increasing fear and worthlessness, I make fourteen calls to the Samaritans, but am unable to communicate effectively with them. I don't know how to open a conversation about the weather, let alone my *feelings*, and I feel trapped, guilty because I know what it is like to be bereaved in this way myself.

Finally, the Community Mental Health Team tells me that I need a consistent care-co-ordinator to work through "potential PTSD (caused by grief and masked autism) and potential autistic-burnout, which has led to additional complex mental health problems." They say that 'someone' will be in touch by phone to arrange this.

I feel relief bleed through the chaos, despite the ambiguity, despite apprehension about answering the phone call (which they are aware of.) But another two *long* weeks later, I receive the phone call from 'someone.' They tell me that despite my complex illnesses and suicidal intention, I will *not* be able to receive help from any mental health services until I have the results from my autism assessment.

> They don't want me, is the soul-destroying message I hear.

Jack asks my GP to speed up my autism assessment referral, so that the mental health team will support me with the four clinically diagnosed illnesses, but she sends the chase-up letter to an autism *charity* by mistake.

Due to a lack of help, I feel I have no choice but to give up on mental health services and integrate back into work. Working is my purpose, my passion, my structure, my normality. I find it difficult to communicate to other people about what is happening with the mental health team, because I feel responsible for it.

But I am too ill.

Inevitably I am signed-off sick, twice, by an occupational health psychiatrist, and sent straight back to the Crisis Team both times, *without* a plan in place to be able to return to work.

It feels hopeless.

One bad-mad night, Jack contacts the emergency crisis number that the Community Mental Health Team have given us, and is told to *"take her to A&E if you want, but unless her leg is hanging off, there isn't a lot they can do."* I wish my leg *was* hanging off. Anything to get 'someone' professional to understand this invisible, uncommunicable pain, get me back to work, back to being a caring teacher, friend, sister and daughter.

*Something black and ugly in my brain calls me unrepeatable names; flashes violent thoughts and images through my mind insistently; drains my energy; tells me that I am bad, draining, worthless, pointless, awkward and unlovable. It tells me that everyone will be better off without me.*

I go from crisis to crisis. There is no break from it. I try hard to escape the bad thoughts but they *follow* me everywhere. They tell me things. I believe it all. I listen to my mad mind's instructions. I make an attempt on my life and am taken to hospital.

*It isn't me. It is a monstrous, mind-consuming beast-illness that takes over me. I don't even believe I have the right to take my life, but I do believe that ending my life is the only cure for this pain, this confusion. Everyone will be relieved because I will be at peace and they can continue their lives and jobs unburdened.*

Before being discharged from the hospital following another suicide attempt, I have to be 'assessed' by mental health to make sure I am 'medically fit'. *But I am not allowed anyone with me.* When Jack tries to accompany me the mental health practitioner tells him to sit and wait outside because we are "only going to be a few minutes." She asks me if I had wanted to die, so I say "*no*" because it is what she wants to hear. The reason behind my suicidal intention is longer than "a few minutes," she looks impatient, and Jack isn't there, to help me process her questions, to help me communicate in a way she will understand. She questions the 'potential autism' on my notes because "my eye contact with her is good."

*She tells me not to do it again.*

*You didn't try hard enough, you didn't try hard enough,* is the message I hear.

I am discharged with an ironic, hand-written 'care-plan' of self-help websites, and already a plan in my mind to *try harder next time.*

That was eighteen months ago but my memory of those months is like fog. Yesterday, after finding out that my new care coordinator had gone on maternity leave without reallocating, or even *telling*, me, I took myself to the mental health team in crisis, with a carrier bag filled with medication I had collected - medication for a new diagnosis of bipolar disorder. I asked the receptionist at the hospital, in the midst of my irrational state, if she could take the tablets away from me, because I wanted to give myself a chance of winning against the instruction of these wretched, relentless thoughts. It took a crazy amount of courage - I never ask anyone for anything. She made a phone call to someone, to ask them what she should do. Whoever it was she spoke to told her that they "weren't allowed to take them," and that, despite social anxiety and suicidal intention, I would need to deliver them to the pharmacy in Tesco's myself.

The thought occurred to me afterwards that I would probably have received more support if I'd taken myself, and the tablets, to a local shop, library, pub … anywhere but that mental health hospital.

Too many people with diagnosed (or undiagnosed) autism develop mental health disorders because of the disorientating feeling that they've been born on the 'wrong planet.' They are unable to find the help and support they need from professionals in the mental health services because their brains work differently. On a social media group for people with Asperger's Syndrome, a member asked what everyone's co-morbid conditions were, and nearly everyone replied with long lists of clinically diagnosed mental illnesses, misdiagnoses, and stories of rejection, miscommunication and fear. There is not enough autism training for the dedicated mental health practitioners that *do* want to access and communicate with autistic people and help them.

This leaves us with little hope.

> *Too many autistics have recurring suicidal thoughts, or have made attempts to end their lives and, in the autism population, suicide is just as common in women as in men because of the desire to succeed socially in a society that doesn't know how to accept them.*
> *I am one of them.*

Autism is *not* a mental health disorder, but autistic people are susceptible to mental health disorders because of bullying, masking, isolation and a lack of support.

Addressing this would change everything.

*Just think how much of this world relies on social communication and interaction.*

*Everything.*

Autism makes the process of identifying, communicating, coping with, and recovering from, mental health difficulties, much harder. Lack of acceptance in society means that, no matter how hard we try to belong, we will always be isolated if society doesn't meet us half way; communication is a two-way responsibility. Lack of autism training in the mental health service makes us feel like we are just not important enough to save.

That was a series of unfortunate events (the short version).

# Get 'It' Before 'It' Gets You

If you think that *you* have internal 'traits'
of autism that impact your life negatively
it's never too late to be assessed.
I recommend you keep a journal.
Ask your GP for a referral.

It might be that you *are* 'on the spectrum.'
Either way it's worth reflection.
Your 'traits' might alternatively
be stress, anxiety, OCD.

The message here is that it's best to check it.
Hiding anything makes you wretched.
Do research and think it through.
Get 'it' before 'it' gets you.

And if you find yourself 'on the spectrum',
your life can take a wonderful, new direction.
Autism *isn't* anxiety, struggling and stress.
It's about experiencing the world differently.
Different, but not *less*.

# Depression Takes and Takes

The mind is the worst part of your body that can break, because surgery cannot remove it or fix it. You can't *amputate* the mind. Pain-killers cannot relieve its pain, anti-depressants can only mask it, and we know how serious masking can be.

Depression is an illness of the mind so severe that people have to kill themselves to get away from it. Loved ones blame themselves for that, in a way that they do not blame themselves for death from any other life-threatening illness. *Nobody* is immune. Not men, not women, not children, not the elderly, not the rich, not even animals. The word 'depression' doesn't express the spite and cruelty of it. It's not even *close*. It doesn't sound vast, dark and endless enough. *And what if your broken mind is 'different' to begin with?*

> I don't have depression and anxiety because of autism.
> I have depression and anxiety because other people don't understand
> my autism, and it makes me feel like a bad person.

Even in this day-and-age, people still neglect to open up and face the gravity and reality of depression. Perhaps if we paid more attention to the hints and clues from frightened souls who cannot communicate in the 'usual' way, the world would have more people in it.

Depression, like anorexia, is a thieving mind-disease that likes to *take* things. It takes and takes relentlessly, until you feel like *nothing*, and the less you communicate about it, the more it gains power. Perhaps it will steal your sleep first, or your appetite. It will prowl around taking things so deviously that you don't even recognise it is inside you. You tell yourself to ignore it. You're just being silly. *You need to get over it*. But this isn't *you*. Small jobs seem harder than usual. You lack energy. You start to cancel social arrangements, and you're drinking wine because it is *mind-numbing*. Your curtains have been closed all week, you phoned-in sick for the first time yesterday because you had a 'headache,' and today, because you had no clean work clothes and you're falling into all the mind traps.

*That's not like you.*

Think about all the fragile things you keep inside your mind. Your hopes and fears, memories, facts, figures, thoughts, emotions. Your personality, your morals and values, your drive and ambition, confidence and motivation, achievements, beliefs, your sense of independence, your sense of fun, your sense of humour, your sense of *self*. You can break your leg or your back and still have *yourself*. Depression takes it all away. It takes everything away, until all you are left with is a sick, distorted version of your mind that is constantly questioning you.

*Why aren't you good enough? Why aren't you popular? Why aren't you more like other people?*

Depression empties your mind of all that is you, and fills it with diseased thoughts. You can't think about anything else *but* these diseased thoughts, because there *is* nothing else anymore. They are evil thoughts. They are consuming. They are selfish. Depression steals the things around you that you've made into a life (your job, home, hobbies, friends) and then it wants your last breath. But it needs *you* to do it. *You* have to take your *own* life. Depression doesn't want the blame for *that*. It can torture you, but it can't kill you on its own. It wants *you* to take your life, and break your family's hearts so much that they die too.

That is how contagious it is.

How else can depression convince you to take your own life, other than to tell you you're bad, toxic, worthless, and unlovable? Everywhere you look, you see evidence that these thoughts are real and true. It hurts more than any physical pain could *ever* hurt you. Depression heightens your senses, because it wants you to notice every *hint* of rejection, to overthink *every* facial expression, *every* text message. You believe that you can hear people's thoughts, even when you're not with them, because you are now being totally and irrationally controlled by depression.

People are thinking everything you think of yourself: she is bad, she is pointless, she is autistic so don't talk to her, she is a burden to her family, she is odd, different, she is draining to her friends, her *poor, exhausted* friends, she isn't even *trying* to be better, she is an attention-seeker, she is *so* selfish, so *self-absorbed*, why doesn't she just kill herself if that's what she wants, get it over and done with.

And then, the trouble is, you are isolated. Depression has forced you to isolate yourself because you are a burden upon others; you are even a burden upon the NHS. The mental

health team cannot access you because their system doesn't allow them to, and because you are autistic. You don't deserve medication, fresh air, company, or anything that will make you feel better because you are *bad*. The only thing you can do now is hurt yourself, physically, make the pain visible to people in a last attempt to get someone to listen.

When you are isolated, the bad thoughts are louder. There is no life outside them. You can't ask for help when you are under the spell. You don't even *believe* in help. Depression is all you know, it is familiar, a comfort. Depression tells you death is for the best, and you calmly believe it. You don't fight it, it is too *big* for you. You resign yourself to it. You *are* depression now, it's got you. You are not yourself anymore.

But you are *not* depression. The people around you are not thinking all of these terrible things.

Depression is an illness.

It is not a choice. It is not a feeling.

You are not *depression* or anything else your mind is telling you.

It is this thought that you need to take to counselling and dissect, *today*. You need someone clever to help you separate yourself away from it somehow, because it is not *you*. You are still in there somewhere. You can beat this, people do, and when you do, you will have the gift of experience and understanding. You will have expertise. Opportunity. And if you share your gift, your experience, your understanding, you can help, and save, *others*. Let that be the light at the end of the tunnel, the silver lining. Feel it. Write it all down. Share it. And when you get *yourself* back, I guarantee you will *never* have seen the world looking more beautiful.

# How Do I Feel?

People think that it is difficult for autistic people to identify and communicate their emotions and, for me, this is true.

I am an emotional person.

I experience all of the emotions intensely and I have a great deal of empathy when I see other people reacting to their emotions, but I struggle to name my own feelings. This means I also struggle to pay attention to the messages my emotions might be trying to send me. I struggle to adapt, express and regulate feelings because I don't know what they are.

When I don't know what they are, I ignore them and focus harder on my work, because not-knowing is very difficult.

It doesn't help that my reactions to emotions seem so different to everyone else's.

The emotion I am most familiar with is fear. Autistic people are always frightened and, although that sounds like a sweeping statement, there are studies emerging that suggest that the autistic brain is physically more anxious than the non-autistic brain. Some studies suggest that autistic people even breathe differently.

This makes a lot of sense to me.

There is such a lot to be fearful about, even on the calmest day, when the world and the people in it don't naturally accommodate you. These fears don't just arise on bad days; they are there on good days as well; they are constant. The fact that fear is one of my most familiar emotions makes sense because it presents itself very physically, very powerfully, and it works rather like an alarm to keep me safe.

Despite this, I mask and deny what I now recognise as fear, for two main reasons. The first is that I am not confident at connecting the sensations and behaviours in my body with the thoughts in my mind, and I am hard on myself ('*if they can do it so can I*'). The second is that, ironically, I *fear* any kind of attention related to any of the emotions. Whether the emotion is positive or negative, from joy and excitement to utter panic, I appear to be fiercely calm because I feel like this will enable me to make and keep friends. What happens inside me is worlds apart from what people will see on the outside. I am not

normally a jump-for-joy type of person; I am not a 'scream and cause a scene' person but that does not mean I am not experiencing those feelings on the inside.

Sometimes, when people feel fear, they avoid the situation because of their body's signals, but I walk head on into it. This is difficult for people around me to understand, but it is part of my masking. I continue to focus logically for as long as I can, no matter what is happening, sticking to routines or plans as if the feelings are not there at all. I don't give attention to the fear because my desire to do everything that other people do, without emotion, despite my autism, is so strong. Unfortunately, denying the messages your body is giving you results in overload. This is true for everyone, but autistic overload happens sooner because the experience of the world is so heightened. I imagine that a non-autistic person might experience meltdowns if they lose their child in the middle of a supermarket, if they can't navigate their way out of a thick crowd at a football stadium, if they suffer with panic attacks because of anxiety, or right before they're due to skydive out of an aeroplane. These feelings and reactions are exactly what I feel in everyday environments. When I am experiencing fear, my sensitivities sharpen: light, noise and touch become even more unbearable and painful. This makes me nauseous. The ability to process spoken and written words disappears and I might rock or stim more obviously because movement helps me to think. I don't want people to see the emotion in my eyes so I cannot look at them and I cannot properly process the things that happen around me.

Changes, people, uncertainty and misunderstandings make me fearful, which means the fear is never ending. Even brilliant emotions like pride and excitement can make me fearful because if I can't precisely identify them in myself, I don't know how to control them. This is scary. It makes me exhausted… but even tiredness is a feeling I find impossible to recognise and manage.

My understanding of emotion is visual, like a scale of numbers or like a parade of animals. A mole, for example, seems to me to represent sad feelings rather more than a tiger, a butterfly or a monkey because of the differences in visual appearance or movement. My understanding of emotion is also in the lyrics of songs and film quotes that I can relate to and memorise - to help me vocalise later on - and I find that I can draw emotion better than I can name it and talk about it.

It's these kinds of expressions that need to be explored in detail so that autistic people can communicate and be heard and helped by different professionals.

It's hard to label feelings because I cannot see them, but I am now working on this in therapy. Therapy has taught me to give feelings more respect because they are science, and complex emotions make us human. I have found out that I am able to identify my feelings in retrospect, but I express them more openly in my writing. The question 'how are you?' can still feel threatening because I need time and help to know what the right answer is, and being 'correct' is important to me. Therefore, I will respond with a learned reaction (which happens to be what everyone expects) like *'fine thank you,'* or *'I feel...'* followed by an action/ thought, *'I feel like I should not have said that'* or a sensation I definitely know: *'I feel prickly.'*

In the past, this 'disconnection' I have from my feelings has been useful. I am calm in a crisis, rational and logical. I am never too busy, too tired or too sad to help someone else. I put other people first because I am not only intuitive to *their* feelings, I absorb them as my own, and it is easier for me to help others with their correctly named feeling, than to stop and figure out how I might feel, what I might need, and what to do about it.

If you identify with this, I need to share two warnings from personal experience. Do not let other people take advantage of your ability to 'cope' and do not be fooled; just because you cannot identify and respond to your emotions does not mean they aren't there. Emotions don't just go away when you ignore them: they build up and burst out in peculiar ways. We need society to accept whatever we need to do to look after our feelings and keep well … even if our coping mechanisms are different to other people's … as long as it doesn't hurt anyone else.

# My Song is Gone

All of my life, I've been singing
From birth, until thirty-years-young
A lyric for all situations
A tune on the tip of my tongue

I sang, in the choir, as a schoolgirl
At church, at the top of my lungs
Never a moment of silence
A girl with a heart-full of songs

I sang because music inspired me
Throughout the good times and hard
When I sang, it was always uplifting
In the bath, down the pub, in the car

One day, the dark overwhelmed me
All black, like the octopus-witch
Stole the songs I'd collected inside me
Altered my mind, my spirit

Now there's no music within me
Now that the songs have all gone
I'm afraid if I sing just a little
I will let out too much emotion

These days are ever so empty
The weeks are ever so long
My heart is ever so heavy
Since darkness stole all of my songs

All I do now is just listen
And watch my friends as they sing
Longing inside to stand with them
In the choir I used to be in

# Can You Make Friends If You Don't Know Who You Are?

*The psychiatrist thinks I am autistic …*

But I don't *want* to be autistic. Please don't let this be autism. The only autistic people I know are boys under ten and I am a thirty-one-year-old woman. How will I ever be able to explain to people that I am autistic? It can't be right. His words flick a switch that transports me back in time.

I am four years old at a playgroup in Shirley, Southampton. The other children are peculiar: they are 'cooking dinner' and 'talking on the phone.' Someone should tell them that it's *not real food.* I sit in the quiet corner, alone, and practise writing my name over and over again. I like the shape of my name; it's a bit like a train, and it's never going to change.

I am five now, and in primary school. Nobody has taught me how to make friends yet,

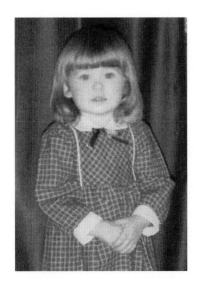

but I've had a go on my own. I like the boy called Henry. He has splints on his legs, a patch over one eye like a pirate and a trache in his neck that makes him whisper. Every lunchtime I sit in the middle of the carpet and cry desolately because everything is chaos and I'm not the teacher, so I can't control it. My teacher's assistant goes home at lunchtime, and I can't understand why. Nobody tells me anything.

The teachers have said I am not allowed to play with my brother, who was in a class below me, at lunchtime anymore, *but they didn't explain why.* They also told me I 'caught the sun', but I definitely didn't do that. They are angry with me because my handwriting is so small, but I keep it small on purpose so they can't see my mistakes. I have to find some control somewhere.

I am six and today at school I had to draw a picture of my best friend and write about them, and, even though I like all the children in my class, I write:

My best friend is a yoghurt pot. She is called Waitrose Fruits of the Forest. She is about 4cm across the middle and she is not a normal shape because she is in between a cuboid and a cylinder. I am so sorry my baby brother took her lid off and ate the yoghurt out of her. I asked my mummy not to throw her away, so mummy uses her as a paint pot now.

I am nine and I have made a decision to never be sad or negative in public because it makes other people sad. When ever I am sad or scared people seem to act like I am trying to be trouble. I can *make* friends now, but I don't seem to be able to *keep* them, which feels even worse. I watch them, I copy them, I try really hard to like the things they like and I do whatever they say, but we just don't *connect*. I don't know my own favourite colour, favourite song, or favourite food but I remember everyone else's off-by-heart. I don't know how to choose favourites. No one ever taught me. Besides, what's the point? I sit inside and re-read *Jane Eyre* to my friend Reuben. He has a wheelchair but he can walk in swimming pools and he gets top marks in all the tests. I am so proud of him. People don't expect him to do things he can't do, but people expect me all the time to do things I can't do.

*I'd like to change my name now, to Jane Eyre. I have a feeling I could be her, better than I can be me. Jane Eyre is my granny's favourite book so I know it's safe to like it.*

I am eleven and am starting a girls' secondary school called St Anne's but *all* the other children I know are going to Romsey School. I don't mind that at all; it's just that girls are somewhat *alien* to me; I am most concerned about missing the school field we had at our primary school and I cry myself to sleep over it.

I went on my first sleepover, but I had to go home in the middle of the night because I "missed my bike." There's a group of girls in my maths class and they are 'popular'. They've grown out of things that I still like. They walk differently down the corridor, they wear their uniform differently; everything they do is different to me but I yearn to *belong* with them.

That night, I write them a letter presented like a 'Wanted' poster, in which I list all the reasons why I would be an excellent friend to have. I am thoroughly reliable, I am loyal, I am honest, I respond well to direction. In my mind I cannot think of a good reason why they wouldn't be my friend. I am giving and good … aren't I?

They quickly conclude that I am not worthy of being a part of their group, so the answer is "no." They give the letter back to me and make fun of my Winnie the Pooh pencil case because it is "babyish," but I think everything about the creations of A A Milne are classic and genius. That's why my guinea pigs are called Winnie and Piglet.

*So I stop eating and get a new pencil case. I have to find control somewhere.*

There must be something wrong about me. Something like shyness or

unnaturalness, but stronger. Some sort of malfunction stopping me from quite fitting in. I am inaccessible, bad. I have a different set of values. I am becoming more self-aware. I wonder if I am a nice person? I don't really *mind* being alone; I like it and *need* it. I like ordinary things like cycling around the birch tree outside my house, imagining what I'll call my children when I am older. I like bouncing my orange ball up and down the garden path as I write animal stories in my head. I like reading and running and thinking about song lyrics. I like teaching myself how to play musical instruments and choreographing dance routines in my head whenever I hear music. I like fixing things and finding out how things work like brains, cranes and hearts.

But if anyone asks I'll say "I like hanging out with friends and going to the cinema."

*I'm fourteen and I'm bullied by a girl who calls me 'mousey' because I am small and quiet but there's no point in talking about it because I'm obviously not a mouse, and if this is the 'common sense' everyone talks about, well I'm glad I lack it. The one good thing is that it's making me work harder in the gym at lunchtimes and my brain tells me that people will like me more if I am skinnier. I've developed an anxious habit of scratching the skin on my arms, deep, until they bleed, but I'm telling people I don't know how it happened, which is a lie. The wounds look ferociously angry and that's how adults will be if they find out it is self-inflicted.*

I am sixteen and I'm hyper-focussed on passing my GCSEs but I can't cope with the emotion. I am clever until I have an exam paper in front of me. My 'cohort' are choosing between going to Barton Peveril College or Peter Symonds College. They are both huge and prodigious colleges – so many rooms, so much movement to process. I don't know how to choose, so I decide to stay on at St Anne's, whose Sixth Form College has thirty students maximum and five in a class: quiet, normal, familiar. Both my grandparents have died and my baby sister has been born, so things at home are rather different. My gran would often joke that I would *never* leave St Anne's, and that I would probably end up applying for a job in the school kitchen and stay there forever. I've learned that I am good at helping people revise, even if I don't study their subject, because I can learn lots quickly and simplify things in memorable ways. Lots of people are telling me I should be a teacher when I'm older. I've only walked out of two French lessons in the past two weeks.

I am eighteen and off to university to study English and Creative Writing and, after a lot of thought, I decide I *am* going to smuggle-in my cuddly toy cat called 'Anxious.' On my first morning in halls I get up extra early, shower, get dressed, put my make-up on, open my bedroom door wide and sit on the edge of my bed in silence with my backpack on my back, waiting for the other girls to get up for the canteen breakfast.

I am not quite sure how to *be*. The older I get, the harder it is to keep up and conform to the social expectations of my age-group.

The girls *laugh* at me, pleasantly.

Some of them roll out of bed and rock-up in their pyjamas: they are funny, friendly. I feel foolish. I expect none of them had laid out their clothes, practised appropriate sentence-starters in the mirror, or slept with their breakfast cards under their pillows.

Why can't I just be *normal?*

Despite sudden bereavements amongst my friends and family, I became a teacher at a local primary school at the age of 22. I also joined my first choir, Love Soul Choir, in my free time, to have a work/life balance and to meet new people. I'd overheard someone in the staffroom say that "that's what functional people do." It was one of the best decisions I ever made, and it was where I first met Jack and his best friend/housemate, Love Soul Choir director Dan Cooper, who would become another great friend of mine.

Jack and Dan 'get' me.

For months Jack was my ears and my voice at appointments with my GP, the crisis team, and different professionals in the mental health services, when mine had seemingly shut down. Without his intervention at this time, I would have been too ill to pursue 'help' on my own which makes me scared for people who don't have a friend like Jack. I would never have been able to manage my medication, get myself to the hospitals, or even open the door to let the crisis team into my home. Jack was able to communicate the things that I was unable to say, to answer questions, and fight them for me, when I was continually falling through the net.

I expect I am not even aware of *half* the things Jack did for me when I was ill.

I became friends with Jack when he was directing Love Soul choir with Dan, but I left Love Soul when I got into a relationship and moved a little way out of town. When the relationship ended, I planned to join Love Soul again, but Jack was starting a new choir, a 'sister' choir, so I went along to *Sing Now Choir* for a fresh start. I consider *Sing Now* to be my second family, especially Jack who is like a brother to me.

Jack's company energises me and we always know what each other is thinking without using words. I don't over-compensate, overthink or hide behind any masks when I'm with him.

I am just myself.


"Tell me about friendships throughout your education," the psychiatrist says.

"There's never been anyone I haven't *liked* ..." I explain, "... there's been many that I believe I have *loved* and there's been unspeakable loss.... I never forget a person. I think of them ... even the people I am no longer in touch with. I wish only good things for them. I know a lot about people because I listen and I watch, and I fix things that they find difficult, yet the older I get, the harder things become and the lonelier I feel."

*I think that's why I like cats.*

He listens, interested by the fact that many of my most successful friendships have been with boys or with people who are very obviously physically different to me. He says that it is "something to chew over."

*The psychiatrist thinks I am autistic...* Despite my nerves, I finally tell my mum, over coffee at the Robin's Nest Emporium, an antiques market.

> *It is like a light bulb has gone on in her head.*
> *Neither of us had ever considered the suggestion that I might have autism,*
> *but now that it was being suggested to us, it seemed to make*
> *complete sense.*

# LIZZY THE LION

By Claire Murphy, Aged 7, Tuesday 13th July 1993

Once long ago there was a lion called Lizzy.

She wanted to make friends with another lion called Lucy.

One night, Lizzy was so tired that she fell asleep on the top of her cave. She went to bed thinking "I will be alright tomorrow." She went to bed in a very good mood. But suddenly she panicked that she will not be alright tomorrow. And then she couldn't get back to sleep.

She went to look for a friend with a very clumsy walk.

She found Lucy asleep inside her cave. "You think you are a better lion than me," said Lizzy in a big loud voice that woke Lucy up from her sleep.

"I cannot be bothered to shout and scream at you at the moment," said Lucy. "Go away to bed." So Lizzy went back to the top of her cave.

By morning she was with the Gods who were very very angry because they said Lizzy was spoiling their birthday parties.
They gave Lizzy a punishment.

The punishment was that they were in a hot place. So they banished Lizzy all the way to the North Pole forever so that she could die.

Meanwhile Lucy became popular because she was a good roarer.

The End.

# LILY AND THE TREE

By Claire Murphy, Aged 7, Wednesday 9th September 1993

Once upon a time there was a little girl called Lily.

She was reading a book on her bunk bed while all of the other children played outside.

Her mummy called her and said "Let's go to the woods." So Lily stopped reading and went to the woods. She went to the woods with her mummy. When they got there something touched her.

"Did you touch me mummy?"

"No," mummy said.

"Who touched me?"

"It must have been that tree." Mummy said. "It is a magic wood."

"That is wonderful," Lily said. And then Lily said to the tree, "Do you want to be my friend?"

So mummy went home and Lily and the tree made a pretty party in the wood.

They had a good time because Lily had a pretty dress on and the tree had a bow tie on. When some of the leaves fell off the tree onto the ground Lily picked them up and put them back on the tree where they came from so that it did not hurt.

"Thank you," said the tree.

So Lily and the tree decided to live together and it was fun for them.

The End

# Diagnosis Day

*July 2017: The mental health team won't help me with mental health until I've had the autism assessment, but I am losing my job, my home, my will to live. Every time my GP chases up the autism assessment referral, they add on another six months.*

The National Autistic Society provided me with a list of organisations in my area that were qualified to conduct the autism assessment privately, and I researched them with the support of Jack to find what I felt was the most thorough and expert diagnostic assessor.

The assessment was conducted over two days.

I attended the pre-assessment with Jack. Prior to the appointment, I had to fill in numerous questionnaires and post them to my assessor, so that she could analyse the results according to criteria to which I was not privy, and it was suggested then that I should attend with a friend who has known me socially for a significant number of years. I discovered afterwards that the questionnaires were measuring depression, social communication and interaction, restricted interests and repetitive behaviours, social awareness, social cognition, social communication and social motivation.

Jack and I are welcomed into the assessor's office and we sit on her sofa. She sits in the far corner, and I sit on my hands. I get strange lines, numbness, redness, and pins-and-needles when I do this, but I feel like it helps me to control my body, control my breathing, and control *everything*. If I sit on my hands, I am more compact. I cannot do anything odd with them or pick the skin on my head or suck my fingers.

Her job is to pre-assess me, and pre-assess Jack, for *his* knowledge of me as a close friend. Jack is honest, open, confident and eloquent. I am literal, guarded, anxious. Hiding inside myself. Jack filters out the environment, so he can focus on the assessor. I am concentrating on making eye-contact with her but it feels like I'm looking directly into her brain. The psychiatrist at the mental health hospital had said that my eye-contact was 'poor.' His *haircut* was poor. I am hyper-aware of my eye-contact *right now*. I'm not sure if I am over-compensating, over-staring. I am obsessing so much over which eye to make 'contact' with that I am not processing what she is saying.

I am 'managing overload' in my own autism assessment.

By the end of the pre-assessment, the assessor has gathered enough information from my questionnaire results, and her interviews and observations with Jack and I about my social ability and experiences of the world, to recommend going forward with a formal autism assessment. The scores on the questionnaire I had submitted ranged from 'within normal limits' (59 and below,) 'mild' (60-65) 'moderate' (66-75) and 'severe' (76 or higher.)

I scored '*severe*' in every category except social awareness.

I didn't go there wanting a diagnosis of autism. I just wanted an answer, yes or no, so that the mental health team would be able to help me.

I believe that it is my social awareness that makes the impact of my autism on me and my mental health so 'severe', and the impact on those around me so 'mild.' It makes sense to me that self-aware autistic people are more likely to mask their difficulties and experience burnout and severe mental health problems, in exchange for 'fitting in.'

My mum attended the formal assessment with me.

A significant part of the formal assessment was based on my early developmental history, dating back as far as birth. Mum told the assessor that I was born one week overdue, with the cord wrapped around my neck and my body. She joked that even as an unborn baby, I preferred the sameness of familiar surroundings and didn't want to come out. We had to remain in hospital for a few extra days before going home together. I was breast- and bottle-fed, and most of my earlier milestones were met on time. But I had issues with sleep and with attachment. I would wake, distressed, if ever my mum left the room. Mum described me as having a 'sixth sense.' I could sleep through her doing the hoovering around me, but the second she tiptoed over the threshold I would, without fail, wake and cry.

As an infant, my sleep and eating schedule was rigid and did not vary. I was never a fussy eater exactly, but I did not tolerate the textures of soft or 'sloppy' food, like cauliflower cheese, mashed potato, and rice pudding nor did I enjoy the taste of their colours. I ate for survival rather than enjoyment and this is still true today. I always slept in my own bed, where I would endure the same crippling nightmare about fire, for years. I experienced anxiety, too, around toilet-training, and had a strict schedule for using the toilet, which I would only use at home. My mum would read the same storybook to me at the same time every day, and I was reluctant to deviate from this routine. My speech and language was advanced for my age, and I would help my brother by speaking *for* him, although the tone of my voice was so soft and quiet that people struggled to understand me, and I would rarely open a conversation, or talk at all unless directly spoken to.

*"As a toddler…" my mum explained… "…she was terrified of shops. I would always bring one of my friends or my sister to town with us, so that I could leave Claire outside in the pushchair with supervision, while I went into bright, busy shops like Superdrug and Boots."*

I had friends and acquaintances but I preferred to play alone. I collected 'Puppy in my Pocket' dogs and would line them up, or set them up in scenes, and the scenes would be identical every single time. I organised the dogs into families. I knew their names, ages, likes and dislikes, off by heart, but I never role-played with them. I found socialising stressful, even with family, and would 'escape' to help my grandmother cook in the kitchen. I mostly played with boys who had learning difficulties. I read books, wrote stories, or rode my bike repetitively round a tree, whilst building an imaginary world inside my head, which I never spoke about with anyone. I had ordinary fears like balloons, fireworks, fire, shouting, banging, people, and parties, but was comforted by the washing machine. My sensory difficulties regarding sound and hearing gradually increased with age and continue to do so. I made up an 'alien' language when I was five, to make my family and acquaintances feel excluded, which I still recall.

On returning home from school or outings, I would experience meltdowns that at the time were seen as bad behaviour but that were actually the harmful result of masking social and sensory differences and of mimicking behaviour all day, even at the age of four. My mum would be the only one to witness this. My teachers, grandparents and friends of the family never believed I was capable of this 'bad behaviour' and always told my parents how "good," "articulate" and "polite" I was. I came to learn that 'sad is bad': I was unable to verbally communicate feelings of sadness so I stopped trying. Besides, my parents just wanted me to "be happy," as all parents do, but I was *literally* desperate to please them. I denied and buried everything that might be considered sad, painful or unfathomable, deep inside my soul where it couldn't hurt me or anyone else, right up until the age of thirty-one.

At the assessment, my mum was questioned for an hour and thirty-five minutes about my childhood and developmental history. It was hard for her to remember back that far. It was hard for her to not know what her answers *meant* about me. Mum was asked to leave the room after that and the assessor began to set up a video camera, because she was going to film me participating in a series of different activities and an interview, much of which I have forgotten, but I will share what I can remember.

She handed me a picture book with no words and asked me to tell her "the story." I flicked through all the pages before turning back to the first page, searching for clarity. I shocked myself because I had no idea what to say, yet I expect even the youngest children at the school where I teach to do tasks like this all the time. The book had no words, so I had no words in that moment. The pictures were beautiful, packed, and busy. But there was no single story in my mind, just fragmented images. It was like walking into a room I've never been in before and trying to process all the information, get it straight in my mind, and then vocalise it.

How would I know if I was telling the *right* story?

Every single page seemed to tell me a different story.

I told the assessor all about what I could *see* on the pages because I knew there was literally no way of getting that wrong. And there was so much to see. I made her notice things about the pictures that she had never noticed before. There were tree trunks with faces in the bark, fields that looked like quilt-covers, chess pieces, a boy in stripy pyjamas, a flying bed, all disguised amongst the pages of the book.

The assessor took the book away and gave me a bag of random objects. I took them out individually, touched them and looked at them. She told me to "make up a little story, using all of the objects." A cork, a cotton reel, a piece of string, a chess piece, a piece of square material, a cocktail stick etc. I lined them all up and I searched them for *clarity*. I had no idea what to do next. This time I had no back-up plan except anxiety. After a long, long silence, the assessor took the objects and made up a little story with them herself, as an example. I listened and watched. Then I took the objects and copied *her* little story word for word.

> She asked if I would normally ask for help when I am stuck.
> I said "no." Asking for help is a complicated skill, and I always feel
> that I should be able to do everything myself.

I wanted to be able to take the objects home, to think about how to create a story and rehearse it on my own with no-one watching.

The assessor then told me to teach her how to wash her face using instructions and actions. That was the only information I had. I did not know the *purpose*. I was self-conscious and over-thinking the possibility of getting such a simple role-play wrong, as I imagine anyone would, and I always have the assumption that if *I* know how to do something, all other adults must know it too. I know for sure that she must already know how to wash her face, therefore what was the point? I followed her instructions and finished by telling her "this is not how I wash my face," just in case I'd got it 'wrong' or explained it in a different order to how she would do it, but I didn't use actions. I know now that she was observing my body language and facial expressions during the whole assessment.

The process was mentally exhausting.

The assessor started to talk to me about some personal thoughts and feelings she was having and made me feel uncertain, like I was an intruder amongst her feelings. I listened to, and understood, everything she said, and I *empathised*, inside, but I felt hesitant because I am not her *friend*. She was talking as if thinking aloud. My instinct is to think of a solution, and make the solution a reality, but I felt anxious that it wasn't my place to offer to fix things for her and that I could come across as patronising or interfering. I wasn't sure if she even wanted or needed a solution: I didn't know what she wanted from me at all. Over the years I have learned that you are supposed to treat strangers and professionals with more distance than friends; I am a doer not a talker, and empathy in words is not natural to me.

I listened intently but I didn't react.

I tried to think about what Lesley would do.

She wrote in my report that I "didn't spontaneously inquire any further" about the things she had shared, which is true. She also wrote in my report that I only offered my *own* thoughts and feelings when I was invited to talk about my cat, Saffie, or my interest in heart and brain surgery, or police cars. But, for the most part, the quality of my responses was 'unusual' or 'inappropriate' or 'abnormal'.

Then she asked me, "How does it feel *inside* when you are sad?"

I zone in on the word *inside* and picture the different systems insid*e* my body: my skeletal system, muscular system, nervous system, my endocrine system, lymphatic, cardiovascular, respiratory, and urinary, my female reproductive system, digestive system. I try to remember the last time I was sad, and how the systems inside me would have changed to respond to that.

"I don't know."

"How does it feel inside when you are happy?"

I try to remember the last time I was happy and how it felt inside. I nearly said 'warm', because of the thought of being 'inside' my warm family home, or how Lesley's son Elliott's chick-pea curry warms-up my insides, or Saffie, or my hot-water bottle on my tummy, but people feel happy in the snow and when they eat ice-cream. The theatre makes me happy. Music fills me up and makes me grasp whatever I am near so I don't levitate away. My heart beats a different rhythm, forces tears out of my eyes of what *could* be joy, but when it is loud I feel sick.

"I don't know."

I think I mainly share other people's feelings: if they feel happy, I feel happy; if they feel sad, I feel sad; if they feel stressed, I feel stressed; if they are angry or scared I try to make it better.

I have all the feelings and none of the understanding. Like singing a song in Italian and having no idea what it means. No-one has ever told me how to identify a feeling, and my reactions to feelings seem to be different or even the opposite to everyone else's. Maybe if I tried to identify one, I would identify it *wrong*.

"I don't know," I said again.

The assessor handed me a puzzle to piece together and I started to breathe normally. I had no idea, until that moment, that I had been holding my breath every time she spoke about emotions.

Conversations always hold me in suspense. It is the anxiety of being unable to predict what someone will say next, and if I will have the right reply. I had lots of different shapes in front of me now that had to be put together to match a picture. It looked complicated, but this one was easy for me. I just really love interacting with shapes.

> *If you're waiting for an Autism Assessment because you feel it will make a positive difference to your quality of life, prepare mentally for having to go over your past in deep detail. It will be gruelling but it is worth it to be thorough.*
> *Take photographs with you to prompt your memory and communication. Write notes to help you remember and explain events in your life, or a list of your characteristics that make you wonder about autism, but be prepared to hear that it might be something else. Write a poem that describes the world through your eyes. Take with you someone who knows you very well and has known you for many years.*
> *Be honest and be yourself.*

# Why?

Autism is the answer to some of the questions I've always had.

Why can I see and feel such overwhelming detail and beauty in the world that the people around me never notice?

Why do the people around me seem to tolerate noise and light more comfortably than me, without pain? Why is noise so hot and light so loud?

Why do the lights on certain TV programmes make my head burn?

Why does a familiar smell or beautiful fragrance fill me with the same pleasure and excitement as a big, expensive present might please someone else?

Why can I not filter out background noise in order to be in a conversation, or hear my own thoughts?

Why do certain clothes and textures sting and prickle my body? Why do light touches hurt, while deep pressure and pain bring me comfort?

Why do overlapping voices make me feel like I'll explode?

Why am I afraid of public toilets?

Why is it that I can dance and run down stairs, but not step onto a moving escalator without great concentration?

Why do I never feel tired, bored or thirsty? Why am I not 'in tune' with any of my body's needs?

Why have I never chosen to go on holiday, stay in a hotel or go on a rollercoaster?

Why does a small change of plan lead to such intense feelings of panic, overload and withdrawal?

Why don't I know things about make-up, fashion, skin-care, hair and other things that other girls not only know about, but value?

Why do I often resort to being alone or doing things alone?

Why can I communicate effectively with children and animals but not adults?

Why do I ask 'awkward' questions for reassurance?

Why can I not maintain friendships with girls?

Why does it take me so long to process information in certain environments?

Why is social media so overwhelming?

Why have I never had any confidence? Why does self-doubt lead me to say things and make decisions against my better judgement?

Why do things that make sense to others seem so nonsensical to me?
Why does depression and anxiety exhibit itself differently in me than in other people I have known with the same conditions?

Why do I always feel frightened in situations that other people find fun?

Why are situations so black-and-white, right-and-wrong to me? Why is my sense of social justice so strong regarding other people?

Why do I always feel a step behind everyone else?

Why do I interpret everything literally?

Why are people's social and emotional problems so simple for me to solve?

Why do I turn to alcohol?

Why is eye-contact uncomfortable for me?

Why am I so intent on helping other people? What am I trying to prove?

Why am I always trying to find other ways to communicate rather than verbally?

Why am I so unemotional and pragmatically calm in a crisis or in traumatic circumstances?

Why do I find such comfort in routine, rules, repetition, rhythm, patterns and words?

Why do I strive for perfection to the point of obsession and compulsion?

Why is it I can be this clever, but find everyday tasks and daily living so impossible at times?

Why is the question 'how are you?' so hard for me to fathom?

Why do I feel like I am becoming de-skilled as I get older?

Why are my interests obsessive and all-consuming?

Why do my legs and my tummy always hurt by the end of the week?

Why do I listen to and value my own feelings less than other people value theirs?

Why do I feel other people's feelings so intently, even people on TV or people I don't even know?

Why do I have stims that are hard to control?

Why do I feel so wise compared to my peers in some circumstances, and so much younger in others?

Why do I find myself so frequently in situations where people have taken advantage of me?

Why don't I sleep and why do I never feel tired?

Why are my dreams so vivid?

Why is my memory so good and thorough?

Why do I not understand, manage, or value money and other things I cannot see/visualise?

# Telling People You Have Autism

When you tell people you have autism you will encounter
many different responses, because *everyone is different*.
Try not to be hurt if the reaction you receive
isn't the one you expect or need.

Autism is a misapprehended condition,
because most of the people who speak about autism
are not autistic themselves. They generalise,
and they try to fit everyone with autism
into one 'box.' People don't realise
that *we are all different too.*

You will encounter
people who think that because
autism wasn't diagnosed until 1943
it didn't exist before.

People may think that you "can't be autistic
because you can talk." They might also say
that "everyone is a little bit autistic"
but that's okay.

It's an *opportunity* for you to explain.

Most people won't want to *intentionally* hurt you.
You might even be the first autistic adult
they have ever met. So don't be too offended.
You don't know everything about autism either yet.

Don't judge people when they say the 'wrong thing'.
Judge them when they're not willing
to make it right. Everyone is ignorant
about different things.
Take your time.

You're not going to educate the world
overnight. Remember, you don't
know about everyone else's conditions
and the fights they fight.

Be you. That's all you can do.
The best people will be there for you.

# Lost Girls

Are male and female brains innately different, or is this 'neurosexism'?

It seems that half the internet believes *men are from Mars, women are from Venus*, and the other half believes our differences are learned expectations from our gendered culture. Both sides seem believable. Both sides are researched and written about by creditable scientists and psychologists.

What puzzles me is that, if our brains *are* 'wired' differently from birth, why is the diagnostic criteria for brain disorders the same for men as for women?

It is well known that around four times as many men and boys have a diagnosis of autism than women and girls. Psychiatrists Leo Kanner and Hans Asperger, (famous for their work related to autism in the 1940s) based their research and studies on young boys, and *their* deficits in social interaction, social communication and social imagination. Since then, the definition of autism has broadened and there is more understanding. But still the procedure for assessing Autism Spectrum Disorder is based on findings from the study of *boys*.

There are many reasons why autism is under-diagnosed in females, aside from the assessment being geared toward the 'male brain', aside from the tendency to misdiagnose autistic girls with mental health illnesses, and aside from the NHS restricting referrals due to the long waiting list for assessment and diagnosis.

My diagnosis was late because I am average-bright, quiet, eager to please, self-conscious, and, from pre-school onwards, I developed the art of mimicry in order to hide any social ineptitudes I felt I had. When I was growing up, nobody *knew* about autism in girls, nobody considered it, not even me. People thought high-functioning autism affected supersonically clever, anti-social *boys* and that they would grow out of it before adulthood. My autism sat in the centre of a mind-map of quiet anxiety, masked-depression, secret obsessive behaviour and reticence, but my journey to diagnosis is far from unique.

That is why people call us the 'lost girls.'

*Everyone bundles out to the playground like they love it. Most of the boys play football or bumper cars for the whole time, but the girls flit from one thing to the next without a thought. One minute they are sitting in circles 'chatting', whilst doing each other's hair, next they break off into pairs, holding hands and doing clapping games, or chasing boys, or whispering behind the bins, or playing 'mums and dads' with dolls. I have learned to 'play' hop-scotch near the girls, and look busy. I cannot ask to join their games because I don't know how to ask, I don't know the rules, and girl-pastimes all seem to be based around verbal communication, impulse, role-play and touching. I won't sit on my own like the awkward boy in the next class, because the teachers try and help him join in, and I don't want that pressure.*

My six-year-old self 'masked' furiously well in public to gain approval from my peers, teachers and family members. I thought that was what all the girls were doing. The social expectation for my age-group was much more forgeable then, than when I started to grow up through secondary school.

I trained myself how to speak '*girl*' without knowing that it wasn't my language. I trained myself always to behave in a way that was socially acceptable, based on strict observations of adults and strict direction and rules from my parents, but this acting was (and still is) exhausting. I had no idea that I was hiding a 'condition'. I just knew that I needed to behave in a certain way in order to be accepted by others, and I valued acceptance.

But I was most content on my own, where I could have control, stim, people-watch, breathe and think deeply about things. I did not want to *look* lonely, but I was happiest doing a repetitive activity like skipping or cartwheels or making daisy-chains whilst memorising things, or tapping into an imaginary world in my head. Everything there was far too precise and intricate to be shared. It protected me from the chaos and confusion of the unnecessarily over-complicated 'real' world.

In class, I learned to blend in, the way a chameleon camouflages with the colours of its environment, by mimicking girls' conversational mannerisms and by keeping in the background. Tony Atwood, a psychologist known for his work on autism, said *"Girls are generally recognised as superior mimics. Those with (Asperger's Syndrome) hold back and observe until they know 'the rules,' then intimate their way through social situations."*

Everyone masks something, but masking a social condition is extreme.

My mum was the only person who would see the extent of my built-up sensory overload and mental exhaustion from the day. To her, I was Jekyll and Hyde. To my teachers, for the *whole* of my education, I was an average, conscientious girl. To myself I was false, different, *less* and wrong, and hiding complicated sensory and communication differences. These beliefs about myself grew up with me in the back of my mind.

*I am in Junior School but my infant teacher, Mrs Blunt, said I can still write stories for her. I have been in trouble a lot lately with Mr Millward when misreading social cues, and if he doesn't want to hear my opinion about his novelty ties, he shouldn't wear them. But I have discovered music. I am good at it, I know I am good at it, but I don't know why. I can read music but it's like I don't have to. My psychic fingers just know what to do by magic. I am addicted to it but I am not compelled to share or perform it. I am addicted to reading Charlotte Bronte and Frances Hodgson Burnett, over and over. I listen to the same song,*

You can only hide it for so long before it fights back...

... and the intensity with which it fights will depend on your circumstances and the things you are driven to achieve in spite of it.

*the same audiobook. These things are accidental comforts, obsessions, safety-behaviours. I have fallen out with a girl called Lila because she said you don't spell the word ballet with a 't' but I know that you do, because I actually do ballet every Tuesday. Our mums organised that I would go to Lila's house for tea and to 'play', but my screams got out and got me into trouble. I have never been so scared in my life.*

This masking – a suppression of the authentic autistic state – cannot last. It is exhausting and causes burnout and prolonged mental health issues. Many autistic girls are misdiagnosed with personality disorders or develop anorexia as they get older, before their autism is discovered. Some girls might *never* be diagnosed because they function confidently within their means forever.

A diagnosis is not essential for everyone.

Girls that receive a late diagnosis of autism, like me, often do so following a mental breakdown of some kind, which is why I am compelled to write about it, because *still* the diagnostic criteria is based on the studies of boys. You can only hide an innate neuro-developmental condition for so long before it starts to fight back, and the intensity with which it fights will depend on your circumstances and the things you're driven to achieve in spite of it.

I stubbornly survived thirty years before my autism caught up with me. I was suppressing it to be able to teach, live alone, find love, have a close friendship group and so on, and I didn't know how to navigate the barriers I was constantly facing because I didn't know they were there. The autism started to scream out when the pressured transitions and social expectations of adulthood became too complex and intense to wholly mask anymore. When the sanctity of a book, an imaginary world or a little quiet-alone time was no longer a sufficient escape from all the questions I constantly bombarded myself with. Why are the simplest things so hard for you, Claire? Why are you alone? Why haven't you married and had children? Why must you drink? Why don't you talk to people? Why can't you keep friends? Why are you so awkward, nervous, dull? Why do you keep all these secrets? Why is the world too much for you? Why are you so damned afraid?

*I am in secondary school and it is all girls. At break times I find myself wandering around the school; the same circuit every time. The hall is too noisy and is filled with circles of girls chattering, eating, comparing, competing. The cafeteria is too packed. The library is tempting. I just really like repeating my circuit of the school. It gives me a bit of time to digest the previous lesson and visualise the next. I crave these solitary moments: I can count the stairs, the bricks, and the lockers I walk past. I am not unhappy, but safe: people know that I am good at gymnastics and that I am in the Southampton Squad, and that is enough. I like being known for things I do rather than things I say. I need this alone-time to get through the day, and people don't notice that I am alone when I am wandering – they think I am actually going somewhere.*

Subconsciously masking my autistic differences to fit into different situations that are unnatural to me may have had a *detrimental* effect on my adult relationships and my mental health, but despite this I managed to get a degree, and to work as a teacher for ten years. People have wondered if I would have pushed myself to achieve these things if I had been diagnosed as a child, or whether I would have let it hold me back. I would have achieved these things anyway, since teaching is as naturally engrained in my heart and mind as autism is, and autism doesn't take anything away from the motivation, ambition and drive that I have always, and will always, have within me.

> *Despite my diagnosis, I am still trying to live like I don't have autism, which means I have phases of success, followed by phases of burnt-out depressed isolation, because this is what society wants.*

I know that I am rather more like a cat than a girl. Calm, cautious, curious, observant, independent to a fault. I like my own company. I think in real images. My main emotion is fear but despite a popular misconception of autism I long for affection. I have heightened senses and I am a creature of habit. I battle compulsions to stim, repeat, touch, lick, play, imitate, press my face against the freezers in a supermarket or lie face down on the floor on a train and scream to regulate the sensory chaos.

But you will never see this side of me.

I cope like a normal professional woman, until I don't cope, but at least I have taken steps to get to know and respect myself now and give myself less of a hard time.

I am one of the lucky ones, because my autism was discovered by a psychiatrist who knew what to look for, and I had the support from my parents to pursue a private diagnosis. But there are lost women and girls out there and no-one is trying to find them, no-one accept autistic women, like me, who have been through it themselves.

# Social Butterflies

I would be a great birthday party-planner.

I imagine immersing myself in the detail of it all: the colours, the cake, the food, the dress-code, the invitations, the entertainment, the play-lists, the lighting, and the decorations.

I could tie it all together with a theme.

I could make it really *perfect* for someone.

Going to parties, though, is one of the top ten things I am bad at. This is unfortunate, because I long *badly* to be *good* at it. Sometimes I look forward to parties because I forget that I can only really function effectually with adults one-to-one, but the *idea* of going to a party is magical. I think about what present to buy. I like to make a big effort to find the right card. I worry a lot, about what to wear because I am not fashion-able, and many girls my age *are* fashion-able. I like to make sure that I am familiar with the venue in advance. It is important for me to know where all the doors and toilets are and to experience the sensory surroundings. I like to travel there with a friend so that we can share all the hellos on arrival. Or maybe I can stand and smile and they can talk for me while I nod in welcome/agreement. I plan the timings intricately because I need to know what will happen next, all of the time.

These are not choices and decisions just to be difficult. They are social survival mechanisms rooted in anxiety.

Parties heighten everybody's insecurities.

It is a friend's 40th birthday party at a venue I have not been to before. I travel there with Ruby, my friend from my old neighbourhood. We arrive early. I have 'got butterflies'. In the car, Ruby takes out a lipstick from her handbag and applies it in the rear-view mirror. I am practising, in my head, what I will need to say when I walk through the door. I will say: "Happy Birthday John, here is a card for you." I want my voice and my smile to match and be bright when I say it. I try to predict John's reply so that I can be ready for every eventuality, but the butterflies are getting everywhere.

*I like to know what is going to happen next, all the time.*

I have not been here before. My senses heighten. I hold my breath. The sun plays painfully amongst the leaves. I have memorised the guest-list. The band is at nine o'clock. By 'normal' standards I am hyper-organised. Everyone looks dressed-up and I feel out of place. I feel out of place whenever there are people near me.

I am not sure where the toilets are.

I am starting to worry that Ruby will want to leave earlier, or later, than we have planned and we haven't even walked through the door yet. Ruby is walking faster than my thoughts can process the environment, but I'd rather try to keep up with her and maintain a façade of normalcy than voice my unease.

She has no idea.

I wish I were in bed right now.

Instantly, Ruby and I are separated by the spontaneity of the social situation. She is swept away in a sea of people and I am a fish out of water. I feel dangerously safe when I have a glass of wine in my hand. *It calms my social butterflies.* I am still clutching the birthday card. I haven't said, "Happy Birthday John, here is a card for you" yet, and the words are becoming impatient.

I give myself an instruction to find the toilets since the bar area is noisy. The dishwasher is being unloaded, the coffee machine is hissing and the music is blaring. Someone has got a laugh so loud it could pierce my ears. Even the *carpet* is loud. Made louder by the self-conscious thought that I have been left alone by my friend, with no idea how to join in. The band is sound-checking *over* the music. *Anyone could come up and talk to me now, about anything, at any time.*

*Happy Birthday John, here is a card for you, Happy Birthday John, here is a card for you.*

I am beyond ready to see John. But he is nowhere to be seen and neither is Ruby. Everything around me is overtaking my plan. If only I could pause time while I rewind, or recreate my plan in a safe hiding place or under a table. There are no safe hiding places here and none of the other adults are recreating their plans under the tables. I wish I had come alone now, so that I could just leave. I look at my watch. *It's only been five minutes.*

Things are not how I visualised they would be. Things are happening differently. I tell myself that this is normal because I am not psychic and this is a party. But this does not help me at all.

Where has Ruby gone? I am disappointed because the reason I came to this party was that Ruby didn't want to come alone. Now I am left holding her bag. Perhaps that's my purpose in social situations: the bag holder. I would never have left *her* alone. This thought makes me wretched but Ruby is different to me. She is like dandelion fluff blowing in the wind; her emotions control her tiny world and she is the centre of it.

I haven't seen John to give him his card and I thought this would happen first.

*Happy Birthday John, here is a card for you, Happy Birthday John, here is a card for you.*

I stop looking for the toilets because I look lost when I am wandering on my own and this might attract attention. If someone asks me if I'm lost, I don't want to have to tell them I am looking for the toilets, because then they might show me, and then I will no longer have directional purpose, and that will be awkward. I wish I smoked and then I could stand outside and be in a specific place for a specific reason.

There is a girl with a pretty dress at the opposite end of the bar: her shoes complement her dress impeccably. I wonder how she knows how to do that. I wonder if all her clothes always match like that. Her hair is done in an up-style that suits her. I wonder if I will ever know what suits me, or if that's just part of the social 'girl-code' I was excluded from at birth. Her nail polish doesn't match the colour of her dress but it clashes in a deliberate way. I can't help but think that if I swapped clothes with that girl, I would look a mess, yet she looks absolutely glorious and, now, I am noticing that all of the girls around her are like this too.

She is a creature in her natural environment, comfortable, confident, balanced and popular. A social butterfly. *I copy her.* This is how I will know what to do and when to do it. I will be her mirror image. If I stand how *she* stands, hold my drink how *she* holds her drink, smile how *she* smiles, I will blend in. I will be okay.

Someone unexpectedly grabs my shoulders, spins me round, hugs me hello. It is Ann, a friend of Ruby's. "I'm coming home in the car with you and Ruby," she says. She says it like it's nothing, no big deal, no big trauma. But I haven't got any words ready for her. And this is…. sudden. Will I be dropped off first or will she? Where does she live? What route will we take to get there? What time will I be arriving home now? What if she doesn't want to leave at the time Ruby and I have agreed?

*Happy Birthday John, here is a card for you, Happy Birthday John, here is a card for you.*

I can't stop saying it.

*Happy Birthday John, here is a card for you, Happy Birthday John, here is a card for you.*

Ann looks like she thinks I am angry, but I am scared and Ruby isn't helping.

The words burst out before I can stop them. They are bursting out of me because they have been hanging around in my head for so long that they have become hot and tangled up. And I am a balloon. Not a butterfly like the girl with the pretty dress and her friends. And I am *burning*. And I want to be hidden. And I am about to burst.

The rest is private.

# A Dress Rehearsal

To top it all off, I have a vitamin B12 deficiency.

My GP says I need two B12 injections a week because my body is "not absorbing properly" and it is making me feel extremely unwell. After that I need an injection every eight weeks for the rest of my life. I am unable to stand or walk without breathlessness, unable to shower or climb the stairs without blurred vision and faintness. I have a reduced appetite; I have muscle weakness, fatigue, pain down my legs, a decline in my mental health and more pronounced autistic characteristics. Before I can start the injections, however, I need to have a gastroscopy at the hospital, because, due to additional symptoms, the doctor wants to rule out a gastrointestinal disorder or a bleed.

Not only do I have Crohn's disease and Ulcerative Colitis in my immediate family, it is also well documented that gastrointestinal disorders are among the most common medical conditions associated with autism. So, with encouragement from my friend Lesley, I book the gastroscopy.

During the two-week build-up to my appointment, I find myself watching gastroscopies on YouTube. I view so many that I could probably perform the procedure myself if you wanted me to. Surgery has always been one of my 'special interests' (exacerbated by my great *Grey's Anatomy* binge of 2016).

Something like fright catches in my chest over the next few days and is taking my breath.

I manage to identify (now that I am trying to be more conscious of the messages my body gives me) that I am not frightened of having the gastroscopy at all: it's a simple, routine procedure. The explanation for my anxiety is sensory based and a fear of everything the internet *can't* tell me.

However daring I want to be, if my brain is receiving too much sensory information too quickly, I experience an overload. Autism amplifies everything: Pleasure. Pain. Empathy. Detail. Colour. Sound. Everyone 'on the spectrum' is differently exhausted, but sensory overload for me happens when I mask my condition too much in order to fit in and 'keep up' and it isn't something I can always control…

*The fear of this happening in the hospital is following me everywhere I go.*

So Lesley phones the Endoscopy department at the Royal South Hants Hospital and asks them if she and I can visit the hospital *before* the date of my gastroscopy. She explains to the nurse that it would be helpful if I could come and see the nurses, the waiting room, the procedure room, the recovery ward and all the equipment in advance of the procedure, so that I can visualise everything and know exactly what to expect.

I am stunned at Lesley for having this idea and then for making it happen for me. There is no greater friend than one who attempts to experience the world through your eyes and make things accessible for you.

When I first saw Lesley, I knew nothing about her. I just saw her across the room at choir and thought she looked like a beautiful, bubbly, warm-hearted lady, with kind eyes …

I still think the same now.

Those were my first impressions – I hadn't spoken to Lesley yet but there was a 'connection' I couldn't explain.

I didn't know that we were going to become friends. Why would she want to be my friend anyway? She is older, wiser, and has her own circle of close friends that she joined the choir with.

Lesley came to choir on alternate weeks, because she belonged to another choir too, and they rehearsed on the same night. I found myself looking forward more to the sessions Lesley was at, because she had started to smile at me across the room, and I didn't know why.

We still hadn't spoken, but I had noticed something in her that I recognised in myself … something I was hiding from my peer group. I joined *Sing Now Choir* at a time when I was living alone at my flat and when my life was spiralling downhill a little. My authentic self (behind closed doors) was not the same as the person I presented in public.

I had an inkling this was the case for Lesley too.

Then Lesley sent me a friendship request on Facebook.

We *still* hadn't spoken, other than to finalise the details for a surprise birthday party that I had organised for Ashton, one of the other choir members, but one day I messaged Lesley on Facebook, because I had heard that she was a hairdresser and I was planning all the hair and make-up for the Rock Challenge, a global dance show at Southampton Guildhall.

From that moment, we have messaged every single day, sometimes all day.

I found myself looking forward to getting home from work, because chatting to Lesley on messenger was the only comfort I had at night. She was chatty in a way that I had never experienced. She wanted to tell me all about her family, intricate things about her childhood, and about the things she loves, and I loved her instantly. She told me that she had felt the 'connection' when she saw me across the room at choir; in fact she was the first to mention it. She wrote that she found me "interesting," and "different." She said that my friendship with Ashton, who has some disabilities himself, "melted her heart" and she "wanted to know me."

As time passed I began to share things with Lesley that I never dreamed I would share with anyone. She did the same with me, and we both said that we had never been comfortable enough to share so openly with another human being before.

It was then that I realised my instincts had been correct. She is in pain, she is living in grief, and she is doing her best, every single day, to survive for the sake of others. She has the same picture of trauma in her head that I do, and that must have been the 'connection.' The bubbly, bright mask is her protection, her shyness, her coping mechanism.

Everybody masks something.

The more we talked (while I was camping out on that sofa, night after night), the more I loved Lesley. She praised me for saying things I thought I would always need to hide, out of shame. Her words amazed me, comforted me, energised me and opened me up in a way I never thought possible. We had a right laugh some nights and couldn't reply quickly enough to one another. Sometimes, Lesley would get 'on a roll' and I would just put my phone down and make a coffee, while she sent message after message, because I didn't want to interrupt her flow! We would 'chat' non-stop until 3am, pausing only to put the kettle on or have a wee, and it would take ages to say goodnight, because we would each send about forty goodnight GIFs before logging off. Her name would pop up again in the morning, always with hearts and kisses and messages full of love, and it would give me strength to do my day, knowing that she'd be there when I'd got home and got my bottle of wine, and we could talk all night again.

When I became ill, Lesley stayed close. For months I would not let Lesley help me with anything. We had opened a 'can of worms' in our messages to one another, but I was so frightened of becoming a burden. Lesley insisted and insisted, always saying "helping you helps me."

I can understand this now, because helping Lesley helps me too, and now that I am in recovery, I am there for her every day.

I think we were meant to meet and be friends because we needed each other - we were lonely, and Jack's choir bought us together.

The NHS nurse that Lesley speaks to is understanding, and she organises a date for us to have a tour of the department led by a nurse from the Endoscopy team.

We arrive at the hospital for the tour, and I am an owl today, observing and memorising.

I memorise the walk from the car-park, through the main doors, down the corridor, round the corner to the lifts. Up in the lifts we go to the first floor where you can't get lost because the signs are too clear. The waiting room looks like a normal waiting room: there are chairs around the sides, the TV is on but the sound is off. There are magazines on tables, a long window looking out to the hospital roof and a few posters on the wall. One of the posters tells you what to drink and what not to drink if you want a healthy bladder. A man comes to greet us: he is a nurse and his name is Jeremy Graff.

He talks mainly to Lesley but that is okay because I am concentrating on remembering what things look and sound like. First, he shows me a little office where I will be asked to sign some forms and have my blood pressure taken; then he takes me to a room where I will wait and have a cannular inserted; after that, we walk to the procedure room.

There is no bed there today, but I can stand where the bed *will* be. He tells me that I will lie on my left-hand side and that means I will be able to see a little trolley of medical things and four posters on the wall that are too far away to read. He tells me that the doctor will be called Dr Baines and that he has been doing this procedure at least "eight times a day" for "longer than I have been alive." He tells me that Dr Baines will probably have two or three nurses with him: one will be monitoring my breathing and heartbeat, and the others will be taking notes or standing by my head.

I didn't have any further questions. Everything I wanted to know had been addressed in detail. I go home content, confident, secretly looking forward to it and able to visualise what was going to be happening to me.

My gastroscopy is at midday today and I haven't eaten or had a drink since 5pm yesterday. I know that the doctor is going to inflate my stomach with air so that he can investigate it properly. I know the way to the department so I don't need to consider the worry of being lost and having to ask for help. I recognise the nurses on the desk and they are expecting me: they tell me to sit in the waiting room (like they said they would.) The TV *still* has no sound and the poster is *still* telling me what to drink to maintain a healthy bladder. The nurse I met at the pre-visit comes through the door and calls the name "Claire," but it is a different Claire, and that makes me confused, but he recognises me and says "you're next."

Things begin to happen fast.

Dr Baines is there. He looks different to how I had imagined. He is asking me questions as a nurse clips an oxygen tube into my nose and around my ears. My whole body is shaking. Dr Baines is spraying numbing spray into my mouth. The internet told me that the spray is disgusting but I don't think it's that bad: it's a bit like bananas and now my throat is definitely numb. Another nurse is injecting sedative into my arm and helping me to lie down onto my left-hand side as the doctor tells me to bite on a blue mouth-guard. I think I am sedated before my head hits the pillow, although I am vaguely aware of a metal bowl by my mouth.

I remember holding a nurse's hand.

Next I am waking up in the recovery room and Lesley is there. I am grateful to have a friend caring enough to come up with a way, not only to enable me to succeed, but to succeed *confidently*, and to be there when I wake up.

I am grateful to the accommodating NHS staff at the hospital for wanting this for me too, and for taking that bit of extra time to make sure I could be familiar with the routine and know what to expect.

I got thinking about thinking-around-corners, and realised that there are many more things that we can all succeed at if we go about them differently, creatively and with the right support.

> *People can easily make things worse or better.*
> *My people make things better.*

# She is Like Petals

(A Poem about Lesley)

She is like petals, protecting hearts
Delicate silk, she might fall apart
But she is strong
Stronger than diamonds and prettier
Wiser than all, and wittier

She is like petals
She feels in colours
She cares about others
Warm as a mother

A generous spirit
Hope I can keep it
Don't let me lose it
Please help me share it

She is like petals, humble and modest
Safe as a forest that must be protected
Strong are the rootles that keep us connected.

# Do Autistic People Lack Empathy?

Well done *Sing Now Choir*, for your show 'One Sound: America'.

Well done for every single sound, step, smile. I noticed it all as I watched from the back.

Well done to the noble front rows, the free-styling naturals and the loud, lion-hearted leaders of our proud pride.

*We need you.*

We need the poise of the sixth-row singers that you can't see, but you can't be without. We can't *be* without the belting-gifted, and we are not right without those that get it wrong and carry on. We need the passion of the 'pros' and the passion of the people singing for pure mental therapy.

Well done to those that don't mind heights; those that are fighting their own *bodies* to be able to perform with us; those that feel *guilt* for suspending responsibility for one night only, to sing their hearts out. Well done to the shy and the bravely anxious; well done to the pockets of people that build their own support systems to enable everyone to be included. Well done if you don't give up and well done if you praise yourself, even if you weren't perfect. Well done if you're in the limelight and well done if you're not.

Well done if you did it *your* way.

That is inspiring.

If you mimed because of the lump in your throat, or if you committed to a wrong note and *owned* it, I saw it all and it moved me to the core.

I joined *Sing Now Choir* when it was born, over four years ago now, when there were only ten of us, and we decided to be a *family*.

Now look at us.

We accept everyone into our choir family because singing is for everyone. Together we are young and old, quiet and loud, sick and well, confident and shy, strong and vulnerable, happy and sad. Together we have everything covered: we can sing anything and we welcome everyone.

Even me.

TRUE EMPATHY
REQUIRES THAT YOU STEP OUTSIDE
YOUR OWN EMOTIONS
TO VIEW THINGS ENTIRELY FROM
THE PERSPECTIVE OF
ANOTHER PERSON...
I CAN DO THAT FOR YOU...
BUT
CAN YOU DO IT
FOR ME?

I haven't rehearsed and performed with *Sing Now Choir* for months since depression took the music out of me, but Jack includes me in back-stage work at performances, in singing guide tracks to help choir members learn their harmonies, in choreography, in creative admin, and to be his 'sounding board', a calming support for him.

He gave me creative choir projects to think about to distract me from depression, and to keep me from being isolated by it, and when he explained to the choir about my autism diagnosis, he said that everyone clapped.

*As I watch the choir, I stand in the shoes of every singer I can see, and I imagine the journey they have taken to get to that stage. Everyone has a 'Sing Now Journey': a different reason for turning up every week. Some of it is to do with singing, lots of it is much, much more than that.*

*I watch Ray, eighty-three years old and centre stage; a dear friend who joined our choir for company after losing his wife. I watch my friend Lesley, with all my might wishing that her husband and her mum and dad were seeing what I am seeing.*

Some months ago, someone told me that autistic people *lack empathy*.

I've spend a lot of time worrying about this, wondering what empathy actually is, and if I have it.

During this time of worry I went to see Broadway star Natalie Weiss at the Leicester Square Theatre in London with Jack, our friend Dan, and Jack's family. Natalie Weiss is a phenomenal singer and actress. She shared with us some of the troll comments on her YouTube videos and the nasty last one said "this girl couldn't act her way out of a paper bag." In response, and before my eyes, Natalie Weiss stepped into a human-sized brown paper bag and began to sing one of my favourite songs: *With You,* from *Ghost.*

It took Natalie Weiss *two words* to make tears roll down my face … and she was standing in a paper bag. She made me cry for every bereaved person in the world, and for everyone who has been 'knocked down' and found the strength to respond with this kind of positive, creative dignity.

It felt like she was singing the song *inside me.*

I want to 'get behind' people and give them a hand with whatever they want to do. It's like being a cheerleader, launching people into the air to do something impressive, and catching them on their way back down. Jack says I always support the underdog and it's true. It is amazing, too, the things you can do if you don't mind who takes the credit.

If someone is feeling ill, I want to feel ill *for* them, or do all their jobs so they don't fall behind. I rescue ants, daddy-long-legs, spiders and woodlice. When I see a dead hedgehog on the road, I feel heartbroken for its family. I put myself in the shoes of families on the news *and I feel their pain*. I cry behind cushions when Dan and I watch *Blue Planet* and the prey gets caught by the predator. I find that documentaries about other people's grief make me nauseously compassionate. My body tingled with helplessness when my mum and I went to the vets last week, and she managed to say "… my cat Merlin has died, we think he has been run over …" and yes, the sob-stories on the *X-Factor* do make my tummy flip.

I think this is empathy.

I think empathy means that you 'tune-in' to a person's feelings and share them: a bit like singing in harmony with them. You think about the world from their point of view regardless whether it is different to your view, and you try and rescue them from negative feelings even before they happen, the way I do for my family, Jack, Lesley, Ray, Ashton and other people close to me.

I think empathy might be all the flickery details I notice on a face that tell me if that person is alright today, even if they are on the other side of the room. It might be the different energy that moves between me and a person when they talk about something *important* to them. It might be the strange pang in my own throat when someone else's voice cracks, or when they suddenly talk faster because they have anxiety. It might be the way I can 'read their minds' even when they *don't* talk, because I find clues in the different ways they stand, sit, sound, interact. I never talk over people. I never finish their sentences. I never interrupt and I never turn their stories around to be about me, even when I can relate. I give people *time*, and time is a precious thing.

I do have empathy, often more than the non-autistic people around me.

I do have empathy and sometimes it really hurts.

I take on other people's worries and problems as my own, like an empathetic sponge, and they hardly realise the lengths I go to thinking of how to help them. Do you know how difficult it is to calm anxiety inside you when it isn't even your anxiety?

I empathise with every child in my classes. Their *pride* when they understand things; their *frustration* when they don't; their *misery* when they break up with their friends; their *joy* when they are praised; their *shock* when they fall over; their *delight* when they help another child; their *uneasiness* when there are difficulties at home; their challenging behaviour when they are *anxious*.

When I was a child, I cried when my dad got a new car, because I didn't want the old car to feel rejected by us.

Autistic people *do* have empathy.

The problem is not knowing what to *do* about all the empathy we feel. Expressions of verbal *anything* are not instinctual to some of us. It can be overwhelming, having so many other people's feelings whirling around in your head, which makes it hard to process things right in the moment. If you are a bit expressionless, with poor eye-contact, communication differences and social skills anxiety, it is not always easy to express empathy in comforting words if the intention for sharing is unclear. Communicating empathy, when you have autism, may not feel natural. It might involve saying things that seem empty, that don't completely make sense, or that don't actively fix the problem like "I'm here for you." We do have empathy, but it is kept inside and more likely expressed in actions, or in the way we adapt our behaviour towards a person. It is hard for autistic people to understand that, sometimes, people just want you to 'say the right thing,' even though that doesn't change anything. While you're waiting for my caring words and facial expressions, my mind will automatically be formulating a plan to practically make your situation better.

Autistic people do not generally do things by halves, including empathy.

I see what people need and I fix things for them, without the conversation. I give gifts, flowers, cards and (most preciously) time that I could be investing in my own interests. I attend appointments with them, post their letters, paint their sheds, get their shopping, visit them regularly, drive them around, tick things off their to-do lists to ease their pressures, organise things for them to look forward to and, in those moments, nothing is more important to me.

I see people's problems and deal with them logically when they can't because of emotion.

> *The misconception that autistic people lack empathy is unfair and untrue.*
> *There is a lot of empathy and compassion for others within me*
> *and within so many other autistic people.*
> *Look at what we do.*

# People Change Their Minds

Routine is more important than *food* to many autistic people. It gives me the stamina I need to succeed in daily life.

Routine is a sequence of things that I have been told, taught and shown to do, and I do them sometimes obsessively, because succeeding on the 'wrong planet' is an addictive, proud feeling.

Without a daily, weekly and monthly routine I do not have the self-confidence or flexibility of mind to function in the world. I do not feel *safe*. Days (or even hours) without routines are disorientating. It's like treading water in the middle of the ocean and not knowing which direction to swim in. You panic because you are out of your depth without instruction. You don't know what is coming next and you fear that your autistic mind might not have the skills to process it, order it, or make the necessary quick decisions to cope with it.

*I need to know what is going to happen next, all the time.*

Routines mean that I know what I am doing, so I can have the room and the strength in my brain to keep my other difficulties under control. Routines are my instructions on how to *be* in this neuro-typical world. I learn the routine. I get good at it because I repeat and repeat it. I find comfort in it, and I feel good that I am behaving and succeeding, like neuro-typical people do.

*But of course, life isn't that easy.*

Sometimes plans change, like a red-eyed bull bulldozing through my planner. It changes my direction and expectations, leaving me standing amongst it all with my head in my hands screaming NNNOOO! Autistic people can be intolerant to change in the same way that some people are intolerant to nuts or eggs or pollen or gluten. It's not about liking and wanting routines – it's about needing them. It's all about finding survival mechanisms in order to prevent uncontrollable reactions.

The more I rely on routine, the more devastating it feels when a change of plan happens.

Nobody likes change. But the difference manifests itself in the mental and physical impact change can have on the brain of someone who is autistic, someone who is routine-driven. The impact of change can disable me for days and days.

It is disabling me right now.

On a bad day, when the smallest plan or routine changes, my anxiety flips from zero to eleven in one second. That anxiety hinders any ability I might have had to breathe, adapt and re-plan. It disables me from thinking at all. *I know how to swim, but I cannot retrieve that knowledge from my brain at the moment, because I didn't plan to be swimming right now ... and it's making me anxious, and the anxiety is hot ... and it looks like anger to you, but it's not, it is fear.*

The battle my body fights, to resist the impact of change, leaves me with chronic pain and paranoia that the people around me do not understand.

That is the negative side to change, but there are positives to being a stickler for routine.

I think my dedication to routine is why the behaviour of the children in my class was good. Nothing unexpected ever really happened in my classes. We shared an accurate plan for every lesson together, and I was in control of any changes. Changing the plan sometimes became part of the plan, and we told each other that it is good to make changes for the better because that means we are always learning. We had to remember to communicate the changes very slowly and very clearly, so that we were not confused.

I want the children to feel comfortable with change, because I don't.

We succeeded in the classroom because we were secure. I made us secure. The children were not anxious; I was not anxious. Lack of anxiety meant we had more room in our heads to focus on enjoying the learning. The children knew their places, their roles and responsibilities, their time limits, my time limits, my expectations. And when something out of my power *did* change slightly, we coped with it all together, using clear reasoning, clear explanations.

The more structured my classroom routines were, the more creative and exciting my lesson planning could be.

*Before my autism diagnosis, I wondered why I got along so well with the autistic children, and the children that other teachers may have described as challenging. I think it is because they knew what was going to happen next, all the time. I think it is because I told, taught and showed them everything. I repeated everything. I made things clear. I altered things so they could succeed comfortably because I empathise with those that fear misunderstanding and uncertainty and I respected them enough, as people, to not make assumptions about their experience of the world, but to ask them about it.*

I was one of those children.

I was dedicated to figuring out how the children in my class individually worked because teaching is my autistic passion. I trust the children, no one knows them better than they know themselves. I accidentally taught *all* the children as if they had autism, because I had autism, and it worked.

A sensory-friendly, honest world would benefit *everyone*.

I used up so much energy creating a perfectly secure and consistent world for the children in my classroom that I had no energy left for myself. I didn't have a perfectly consistent world to go home to at night. No-one helped me keep things consistent in my private life. No-one gave me plenty of warning before they changed a plan. No-one explained a change of plan slowly, so that I could understand the logic of it. No-one understood the importance of the routines and rituals in my life and how they are necessary to get me through the day. No-one adapted the sensory environment for me so I could focus on the daily jobs and the shopping I needed to do. Why would they? I never communicated my need for these things, of course.

Instead, I disguised my lack of control, consistency and inability to regulate the 'real' world simply by taking my schoolwork home.

*I need to run my social life like my primary school classroom with the support and understanding of the rest of society.*

But of course, life isn't that easy: people get ill, the weather is all wrong, people move house, there's traffic, people change their hair, the car breaks down, people re-decorate, people's moods change, things get cancelled, people let you down, people are unreliable, people don't do what they say they're going to do, people die …

People change their minds.

People, people, people.

If you are close to an autistic person, you will probably know all this already. You will already know that it is important to communicate everything very clearly: to plan things in detail way in advance; to talk through plans several times before any event; to keep to the plans; to be as consistent as possible; to take time to discuss any changes that need to happen in a very clear manner; to be patient; to be understanding. Why wouldn't you do this with pleasure, if you care for the happiness of your autistic people? If you are close with an autistic person, there is responsibility on both sides. The autistic person needs to be responsible for finding a means to communicate their needs, and the non-autistic person has a responsibility to accommodate those needs and vice versa.

Everyone has needs.

Autistic people are frightened all the time.

Routines and clarity feel safe.

It is hard being autistic, but it is also hard being close with an autistic person. Friendships between autistic and non-autistic people are very special when they work out. I am reminded of this every day when I think about the extraordinary friendships I have, especially those like Jack and Dan, that care to think of me without making me feel like a problem.

It is important that, as an autistic person, I remember not to feel entitled. Autism is an explanation, not an excuse. I must not demand rules and routines from my loved ones, because perhaps that sets them up to fail and the friendship won't last. I cannot and should not try to control other people's social lives as I do my own. Some people thrive on spontaneity and can 'go with the flow' and that is a wonderful trait to have, but my friends need to *want* to get to know my ways and I theirs.

I have to know the people who energise me and spend my time with them.

And autistic people need to learn strategies to be able to belong in the social world independently and keep safe.

Thanks to my autism-friendly friends and my stubborn motivation, I am able to socialise with the right people, even though 'autism' often doesn't want me to.

I have seen some wonderful shows with Jack, Dan and our friend Mike. We went to see *Harry Potter in Concert* at the Royal Albert Hall, where a live orchestra played the soundtrack to the film *The Chamber of Secrets*. That was my first ever visit to the Royal Albert Hall, and I was in awe. Since then we have been back twice. We also saw *Blood Brothers* at the Mayflower Theatre in Southampton and it was one of the most tense, devastatingly brilliant performances I will ever see. This is thanks to my friends who include me, who patiently talk through the plans with me time after time. They tell me what we are going to be doing next, how long it will take, when it will finish, who will be there, where we will sit. They do this naturally and without making me feel like a problem.

And I look after their individual needs, wants and wishes too.

Routine and consistently understanding, trusted friends take the anxiety and fear of the unknown away from autism, and enable me to challenge my comfort-zone, and enjoy new and unfamiliar social times, as a girl my age should.

# Goodbye to an Old Friend

Dear Ray,

Ray. You died at the weekend. I'm not sure if you know, because you made yourself a cup of tea and then you sat down to drink it. That is quite a normal thing to do, isn't it? I don't think you thought that you were going to die.

*I* didn't think that you were going to die.

That Saturday was Prince Harry and Meghan Markle's wedding day. I went to Lesley's to watch the wedding with Lesley, her mum Barbie, her sons Ryan and Elliott and Ryan's fiancé Ellie. We watched *The Greatest Showman* too and it was a bit like what we did on Christmas Day. When I was getting ready to go there, I thought, *wouldn't it be nice to invite Ray*, but it was one of those swift thoughts that flies out of your head as soon as you have your next thought. I don't know if you watched the wedding or not. It's no*t* really important. I am just trying to imagine what you did that day, and how you were feeling.

Last week, you said you were feeling *great*. You said that you felt more like yourself. You had been through a difficult time recovering from that horrid flu. It left you weak and very dejected because you weren't able to do the active things you were used to doing: the walking, the tennis, the gym.

But last Wednesday you looked bright.

I had started to do some cleaning for you, weekly, because you were so tired of keeping on top of it and I desperately needed a purpose, having been signed-off from work.

Before I did your cleaning that day, we had a good chat, as we always did. I sat on your bed and you sat at your computer desk. We talked about the shows I've seen recently with Jack, Dan and Mike, and we talked about the choir. I told you about the big meeting I was going to have at work on Friday about what was going to be happening to me regarding my ongoing sickness, and you listened and gave me some very wise advice.

*I want you to know that I said all of the things you told me to say, and I was listened to. I want you to know that the meeting went very well and was very fair. Even though it wasn't the outcome I had hoped for, I know it is for the best right now.*

You said you hoped (for me) that I would be able to return to work, but that deep-down you hoped I wouldn't, so that I could still be your cleaner on a Wednesday at 10am.

*This made us laugh.*

You're so silly. I said I would just clean in the evenings or at the weekend instead.

It's quite an intimate job, being a cleaner, changing bed-sheets, being amongst all of your belongings and business. I am only realising this now.

It turns out, following the meeting, that I *am* still available to clean for you on Wednesdays at 10am, *and* do your shopping afterwards.

It made us laugh that you would write me a shopping list for Asda, but of course you didn't have to, because I knew it off-by-heart: *5 Fairtrade, greenish bananas; extra special vine tomatoes; sweet oranges; a small bag of new potatoes; a pack-of-four jacket potatoes; free-range, medium eggs; Cravendale, semi-skimmed milk; Kingsmill 50/50 bread with no crusts; Richmond sausages; bleach; Weetabix; frozen peas; salmon fillets; rice pudding and 4 microwave meals.* But you didn't want me to do the shopping last Wednesday, because you had met an ex-police officer friend, who lived downstairs in your retirement block who you'd been to Marks and Spencer's with.

Normally, while I cleaned, you would rehearse the whole *One Sound* set-list in your newly cleaned bedroom. The songs were all in order from *America* to *Livin' on a Prayer*, and you never missed a *single* harmony. It would take me the *exact* length of those eight songs to clean your bathroom, lounge and kitchen, and it warmed my heart to listen to you sing.

Bless you, Ray.

After that you would gossip about all the different people at choir, tell me stories about your fascinating life with your late wife Bett, and about all of the many different jobs and homes you'd had. I loved listening. I loved *Bett* because of the way you spoke of her. I loved it when you said that you had an argument with Bett every single day*,* and that *that* is the secret to a happy, long-lasting marriage.

I think everything you said and did reminded you of Bett. We never had a conversation without you mentioning her. It is the fourth anniversary of her death today, and people are saying that you are with her. I am so happy for you if this is true.

This week while I cleaned, we just listened to Smooth Radio. I was cleaning your bathroom and you poked your head round the door and shouted "is this James Arthur?" I got the giggles a) because it was Ed Sheeran, and b) because I was thinking *why does an eighty-three-year-old man know who James Arthur is?* We also listened to Billy Joel and Simon and Garfunkel.

Two weeks ago, when we were drinking wine on the balcony, we made some plans together. We were going to go to the beach, and get fish and chips, we were going to explore some little country pubs. You told me about your trips to Las Vegas and you said that you might like to go on a cruise on your own. I can imagine you doing that. You said if you wanted company, you could make friends with people by the pool, at the bar or in a restaurant. You told me to have a go at going on a holiday too.

You really knew how to *live*. And I had no worries when I was around you.

One of the last things you said to me was: I'll be eighty-four soon and I don't know what I'll do when I get too old to come to choir.

On Monday, I went to do some shopping for Lesley because she was so tired, and I took it to her house. I remember there was thunder and lightning when I knocked on the door and I hate that. We had a cup of tea and then she told me that she had some news. I said *is it bad*? Lesley nodded. She said "It's Ray," and I said "where is he?"

*I didn't think Lesley was going to tell me that you had died. It doesn't feel right or true, even now.*

I bought her some roses because I know how hard it is to tell people when someone has died, especially because Lesley loves you so very dearly and whole-heartedly herself. You loved each other.

I stayed at Jack's on Monday but I couldn't sleep, so I sat up and wrote a tribute to you, to share with all of your friends at choir.

*You are really easy to write about.*

I think you will have liked the words, and it's sad that I cannot read them to you. Lesley thinks you will have been proud of me. You would definitely have been proud of Jack and Lesley. At the break at choir rehearsal, Jack read out the Facebook status you wrote after the birthday party that I organised for you, and many people laughed through their tears. You were so *missed*, Ray. Lesley thinks this all feels like a dream and that you will be inviting us over for coffee later.

I think this too.

I walked to your retirement flat on Tuesday to give cards to your sister and your friends in the other flats from *Sing Now Choir*. I walked out into the garden and could see your favourite chair though the balcony doors. Your car is still in its parking space.

I am not sure why those things feel so strange.

I rang Ashton, to tell him that you had died, because I was worried he may not have heard. He had left *Sing Now Choir* shortly before I became ill, to join a theatre group in London for people with disabilities. He spoke about you so fondly and said *God will look after him.* I think Ashton is a bit like us, he can't really believe it. When you first joined *Sing Now Choir*, you asked Jack if I was Ashton's carer. Ashton thought that was so funny, he said "she *is* my carer, she just doesn't get paid!"

The things I miss about you are a bit weird: I miss your enormous ears and enormous cuddles. You remind me of The BFG. I miss when I buzz your door and you say 'come on up'. I miss how you called everyone 'babe'. I miss your matter-of-factness. I miss your singing. I miss your home. I miss how you said 'hello' and 'goodbye' to me at the start and end of every choir session. I miss your funny flirting. I miss you going on-and-on about the Sing Now website. I miss our honest chats. I miss your strength. I miss how meticulous you were. I miss you pulling funny faces at me when you're all singing in lines at choir. I miss your stubbornness. I miss you blasting out Barry Manilow in your car when we drove to places.

You're not really a *normal* old man.

I know that you didn't want to clean or change the bed or do the big shopping any more, and I want you to know that I would have done that for you forever, and anything else that would have become necessary as the years went by, just like I will for Lesley, just as if you were my family.

Not many girls my age can say that they are friends with a funny, wise, handsome eighty-three-year-old man like you. I am privileged to have been your friend. Thank you for everything you taught me. I will be thinking of you forever, Ray. I will look after everyone, and I will make sure we do something special to remember you by.

Rest peacefully, Ray Dyball.

Love you.

# Dear Saffie Cat

Dear Saffie Cat
I have now lost my job.
I have lost myself too, as that was
my purpose and identity. Now I don't know who I am.
Don't think badly of me. I don't know what to do
without my job – or what to hide behind.
It happened for the right reasons, but no one understands
that to me it's just another loss. *Another* one.
I will get better and I will get my job back.
I will always be a teacher, Saffie.
Thank you for listening, my girl.

# Am I A Good Person?

I have been reading the Bible since losing my job.

It is reminding me of all the things I knew as a child but have forgotten as an adult, like *remember the Sabbath day, to keep it holy. Six days you shall labour and do all your work, but the seventh is the Sabbath of the Lord your God.*

I would have been smart to remember this instruction.

Due to my dad's faith and our Irish family history, my three siblings and I were bought up to be Catholic. I enjoyed attending church with my dad every Sunday until I went to university.

I was a timid, perfectionist child, the oldest of four children; afraid of getting anything wrong. I know *now* that I was a child with autism, but that I was also born with the propensity to isolate myself, to fall into dark holes in my mind and hold a lot of responsibility that didn't really belong to me.

I kept the dark holes a secret.

Looking back, these Sunday church services were some of the safest moments in my memory.

*I need that feeling back.*

Our congregation was an extended family and our church felt like home. Singing hymns revived me. Going there with my dad was like learning how to breathe properly again, in preparation for the next week of life. The week's anxieties would slot back in to perspective. I was *always* worrying, always catastrophising about the worst possible outcome, but church gave me weekly reassurance that I *am* good: I don't steal; I say kind words; I help people in need; I think of others before myself; I am humble; I am giving and forgiving; I appreciate the environment; I respect my family. I was reassured by the 'knowledge' that I am never really alone, because I have a protector who does not leave me, who created me because he wanted me to *live*. I was reassured by the consistent structure of the church services; the rigidity of the rules; the right and wrong; the smells; the words; the rhythms; the repetition; the flowers; the familiarity; the *belonging*.

I didn't feel the need to question if Jesus really did walk on water or feed the five thousand. I didn't try to literally believe any of the Bible stories. I had faith because my dad did, and his dad did, and his, and I had faith in them. I just wanted to interpret the Bible and apply the messages to my own life in my own way. And I loved reading. I believe that the messages kept me mindful, and gave me strength and rationality through my exams and many other stressful childhood burdens. They kept me grounded through times of teenage angst and gave me good morals. They gave me depth, confidence and comfort and they kept me on the right track when I was tempted to stray.

They made me understand my purpose and value in life.

*God was like a whisper in my little ear, telling me to keep going.*

*When you go through deep waters, I will be with you.*

Sometimes I ponder whether, if I had continued to attend church as an adult, I would have fallen so far down the 'mental health hole.'

Mental illness can strike anybody, anytime, but I think being a religious child gave me a greater determination to be okay. I think it gave me a better, early understanding of the meaning of life. This helped me to make sense of the harder times. It made me silently strong. Our religious community would work so hard together to provide encouragement, support, food and company to anybody within our 'family' who was in need. It would support a family with a new baby, or a person in crisis, better than a qualified Crisis Team, around-the-clock if necessary.

And the church was a place where you could just *go*.

I don't think you have to believe in God to find comfort and peaceful positivity from a church.

For some people, this will sound like brain-washing bullshit. Many people will never be able to understand it. I have been ridiculed in the past by friends for wanting to support my church, the largest non-governmental provider of education and medical services in the world. People find all sorts of different things therapeutic in life: kick-boxing; counselling; choir; nature; tattoos; yoga; binge eating; not eating; reading Harry Potter; self-harm; drugs; alcohol. I, being poor at verbal communication and unable to identify feelings, wanted just to be able to say little prayers to 'something' above that was bringing me comfort, sing some songs, donate some pocket money to the poor and just *be*, in an environment that didn't attack my senses.

People should do and believe what comforts them, since comfort is rare.

*I stopped believing in God accidentally, when I saw my first dead body.*

It was the first time my faith was really shaken. I remember seeing the dead person before me and thinking … you didn't want to live, and now you are *dead*. It did not look like their 'spirit' was going to live on in the kingdom of heaven, even though I desperately wanted it to. Their organs were no longer working: the 'machine' had been switched off forever. Strangely and unexpectedly, the thought of there being no heaven gave me more comfort than the thought of heaven. It is easier to comprehend death as being finite, black-and-white.

This happened at around the same time I left my church and my Catholic girls' school and Sixth Form College to go to university. There were suddenly no rules, no God, no Jesus, no heaven. Everyone was encouraged to do what they liked and be who they wanted to be, as long as they were happy.

Happiness, rather than goodness, was deemed important.

I haven't lived like a Catholic girl since turning seventeen. I am not part of any church family and I lost the purpose, self-belief, sanctuary, comfort and love within me that I had as a little girl. I still respect the faith; to me the world is so scary with all the choice and freedom that is acceptable. I am still interested in all the different religious beliefs of the world. But the black-and-white brain in my head isn't the same as the vibrantly grey world of religion: it isn't the same as the world my friends and family all experience; it isn't the same as the one I see on the news or read about online.

It listens to what it sees, it is heavily realistic, straightforward and fact-hungry. I am not angry with God, but I have naturally lost my faith. Perhaps I now have more room to think about having more faith in myself.

*God doesn't whisper in my ear to keep going anymore, but I hope that doesn't mean I am not good.*

My favourite Bible story is the Good Samaritan. It is about a Jewish traveller who is beaten and left for dead beside the road. People see him struggling but pass him by. A priest and a Levite cross to the opposite side of the road to avoid the injured man. Finally, a Samaritan stops to help, even though Jews and Samaritans loathed one another. That is what a 'Good Samaritan' is: a person who helps people, including strangers, in need.

*That's who I believe in now, for real. Those are the ones I look up to. That is who I want to be.*

There's no miracle in this story, no magic, just human goodness.

People *still* think that the church believes mental illness to be a punishment for sin but in 1953, an Anglican vicar called Chad Varah founded the Samaritans charity to help suicidal people. He did this because he was deeply affected by the first ever funeral he did, which was that of a fourteen-year-old girl who had taken her own life. Throughout his career, Chad Varah had naturally counselled the parishioners that had reached out to him, but he wanted to dedicate himself to suicide prevention, and do more to help those struggling to cope with depression and contemplating ending their lives. The Samaritans still operate on Chad Varah's criterion, that the charity should provide confidential and non-judgemental support.

It was Ray's funeral this week. People were saying that he is back with his beloved wife, Bett, now and that is a wonderfully comforting thought, but I sadly cannot bend my mind around it.

I think I will comfort myself with the thought that Ray is not *without* Bett anymore.

Heaven is in my head, and Ray will live on there, in my memory, with my other lost loved ones.

> *And God never whispered in my ear. That was me. It was me all along. A strong little girl that, although quiet, pushed herself incessantly to be good and to never give up. My goodness and morality came from a happy childhood at home with my parents, a childhood at church, and my own thoughtful interpretations of the Bible stories I heard there, and it is one of the things I am most thankful for in life.*

# AUNT LIZZIE
By Claire Murphy, Aged 7, Friday 11th September 1993

Auntie Lizzie cannot run because she is a very old lady.

She putted all her money into teapots and biscuit tins. She keeped her money in her pockets and in lockets. This is because she did not know that she had to put it in the bank and she had a walking stick to help her walk.

One sunny day Auntie Lizzie left the window open so all the robbers got in. All the robbers came along and stole all the money in Auntie Lizzie's teapots and biscuit tins and her pockets and lockets. Auntie Lizzie did not need to be robbed. Auntie Lizzie needed somebody to tell her to keep her money in the bank but everyone forgot to remember her.

Auntie Lizzie wished she had friends to tell her about the bank.

The End.

# The Bank

I have a storm in my tummy.

I have tasted a lot of bad feelings this week, and I wish I could spit them all out.

It tasted like shame, disappointment and rejection, with a side of public humiliation. I think those are the right names for the feelings I have tasted … I don't like them; they are beige and slimy. Whilst autism *can* be a blessing, this week it has been a curse, a punishment: it has ruined my relationships, mired my motivation, my progression. Distressed me, depressed me, shocked me, isolated me. Autism and self-awareness don't mix well. The more 'neuro-typical' and sociable I have tried to be, the more autism has punished me and pushed me out. The more I've tried to fit in, the more autism has reared its ugly head, distanced me, and reminded me (and the unfortunate people around me) that my brain functions differently.

*This week it has barely functioned at all.*

I wish I wasn't autistic.

Autism makes depression worse, and depression makes autism more obvious.

It's just 'one of those weeks'.

I had been putting off going to the bank for eight days.

I needed to pay money to my psychologist, and to a friend for a ticket to a show. Banks are my nightmare, along with doctors' waiting rooms, public toilets, shops and trains. To function in these places you need spontaneous social communication.

I haven't got this.

I take out my autism card (which is there to help me alert people that I need extra help in social situations) and loiter by the entrance to the bank for fifteen minutes.

Finally, I walk in and suss out the environment: the place is purple and practically empty. I sit down in a chair to triple-check the details for the payments, then edge over to the queue. A sign says *please wait here,* and I am grateful to the bank for giving me an instruction. I know that one of the bank ladies has seen me, but she is not inviting me over. I have already practised what to say when she does.

"I need to pay money into two different accounts."

Without looking up, she tells me that they have been "having lots of problems today."

*I didn't expect this.*

I am not sure what this means because it is not clear. Do I need to respond? Does she want me to say I will come back another day? There is an awkward silence in which I notice her neat black hair, her flawless olive skin and her (what I have heard people describe as) resting-bitch face. I decide not to show my autism card, because it feels all wrong. I already feel inconvenient enough.

*Inconvenient* is a good word to describe me.

She asks me for the details for the first payment, but now there is a queue of people behind me, and I don't want them all to know that I see a psychologist.

"I have written all of the details down for you," I say robotically, as I try to post them underneath the glass.

"Be easier if you just read them out to me," she replies. "My eye-sight is terrible today … what is the name of the account please?"

*I didn't expect this.*

My insides fizz up like a shaken lemonade, and I have the urge to leave the bank, but I am fighting it, I am 'masking' it. I glance over my shoulder at the long queue of people, then down at my notes. "Please make it payable to Wellbeing Psychology Centre Limited," I say.

"Well … *what*? Can you speak up, please?"

I fizz up again.

"Wellbeing Psychology Centre."

I am hot and bubbling. I am not sure what my body is going to do next. I can feel the eyes of the people in the queue staring at the back of my head. I can feel my own eyes fizzling with red-hot water, and I've learned that this is one of the indicators that I am 'reaching my limit.'

I give her the account number and sort-code and she asks me to "check them, then press *enter* on the machine." I realise that I am swaying back and forth in an effort to quieten all the bank-beeps, and to quieten my anxiety enough to double-check the numbers. I clutch the counter to steady myself; she flashes a peculiar look; I am embarrassed.

"You have written Unbeing …" I tell her, "but it is Wellbeing…"

Even though it was her mistake, her rolling eyes tell me that it is *my* fault. She looks beyond me at the queue as if to say *'you are really holding me up now'*. I apologise for myself but she doesn't hear me because she is now slagging-off one of her colleagues to *another* colleague. "You and I have a system," she says, "but if I ask *Callum* to do anything it's a bloody nightmare, I may as well do it myself."

I don't think I was supposed to overhear that, so I am now trying to *unhear* it, whilst giving her all the payment details again and worrying about what the people in the queue are thinking about me. I can barely recognise the numbers when she asks me, again, to "check the details on the machine." I am trying to match them to my piece of paper, but I am overloading. I cannot hold the information in my head long enough to be able to check it so I just press *enter* and pray.

"And the second one?" she says, handing me a payment confirmation slip.

But I have had enough now. I need to leave *now*.

*I am so shaken-up that I am about to spill all of the pressure all over the floor.*

●　　●　　●

I had planned to do a few jobs after my trip to the bank, but I can't do any of them. I drive home and get straight into my bed.

Two hours later I wake up with a storm of bad feelings in my tummy. This week has consistently added to the bad feelings.

*There isn't a single part of me that doesn't feel unlovable.*

I feel *guilty* for being autistic.

I am *sorry* for being autistic.

I know that the world makes other people with autism feel like this too. I am learning that this 'badness' is temporary, and that perhaps next week something great will happen, or I will find someone that will make me feel grateful for my autism or better yet, make me forget it altogether. I have been grateful before, and I will be grateful again. After all, I cannot change anything but my attitude towards it. I have autism. But I wouldn't be *me* without it.

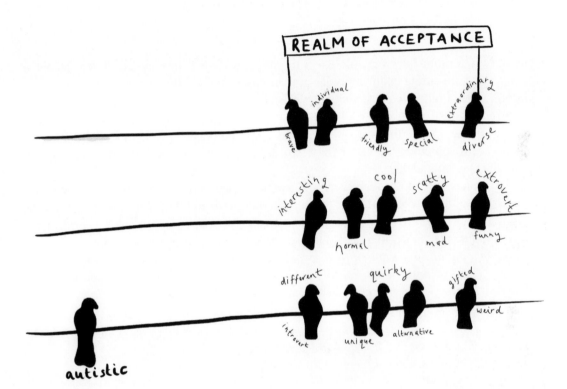

# More Like a Chair

Sometimes in a room full of people I feel more like a chair than a human. I am somehow separate, like I am sitting in an empty jar of marmalade or a goldfish bowl.

I don't mind. I like it in my invisible goldfish bowl.

In a room full of people I am the first to notice if someone looks ill, if someone looks sad, if someone looks different, if someone isn't included, if someone isn't there, if someone needs something … and I fix it. My fixing and my writing are my best ways of communicating with adults.

Fixing things is comfortable because there is a clear problem, a clear solution, and normally (hopefully) validation from the person afterwards to let me know that I have done the right thing. There is a purpose, clear intentions and a clear ending. I am not comfortable with communication unless there is a purpose, clear intentions and a clear ending.

*I am standing at the reception at the doctor's surgery and the receptionist looks at me and says "I've lost my pen." I freeze. She is searching under a pile of papers and I am holding my breath. The words hang in the air and they are heavy and directionless. Why is she telling me? I don't need her to have a pen. What does she want me to do? Does she want me to find her pen? What are her expectations of me? What am I supposed to say? Why didn't she just keep that sentence in her head?*

This happens to me about a hundred times a day.

Most people prefer to communicate verbally with one another, but also use body language, facial expressions, tone and inflection to make their needs and feelings clear. It is exceptionally clever, but I do not function in this way. If you tell me the population of China I will know it. By the same rule, if you tell me you like me, or that you want something, I will know it, but I cannot pick this up from your body language, facial expressions, random statements, 'trains' of thought, hints or behaviour towards me.

I hear words literally regardless of whether they are said in a calm, kind, enquiring way or in an angry, impatient, threatening way. It is like I hear them the way they would be written on paper.

*"Have you put the bins out?" "No," I replied. Little did I know that this abrupt question, bellowed down from the top of the stairs, was actually an instruction. Had he said "Could you put the bins out?" I would have done so instantly, and thus wouldn't have had to endure an entire day of "do I have to do everything around here?" To which I again replied "no" only to learn that this question didn't require a response.*

I am only responsive to the body language and facial expressions of people when they are not directed at *me*, when I am in my empty jar, or my goldfish bowl, separated and observing. Clear facts are comforting to me, even when the thing I am being told is very bad. Without facts and clarity there is just uncertainty, and this makes communicating really scary.

Not everyone wants honesty all the time, but it's hard to decipher when it is acceptable and when it isn't, because the rules seem to change. Lying is wrong, and it doesn't occur to me to cushion truths with extra layers of ambiguous communication. I'm not great with sayings and sarcasm because, even though my brain has learned that they are not meant literally, I still hear everything literally first, and I have to go through a translation process before I can respond. This really slows me down and creates awkwardness.

> *I am only responsive to the body language and facial expressions of people when they are not directed at me, when I am in my empty jar, or goldfish bowl, separated and observing.*

The way other people generally communicate feels to me like a separate language or code that I haven't been told or taught. When I watch and listen to other people communicating I am in awe. So much is said without purpose or intention, so much detail left out, so much small talk and yet everyone seems to know what's going on.

I wonder if they would understand what they just said if they saw it written down?

There is an extra layer of common understanding obscuring everything people say. Their words seem to tumble out of their mouths without them even knowing, without them being affected by additional noise and movement.

That extra layer doesn't exist in my autistic mind; there is no space or energy for it.

Apparently I have to listen to, and understand, what is *unsaid* as much as what *is* said, and deal with disappointment and confusion when people let me down because they "didn't really mean it" or "it's just something people say." I say what I mean, mean what I say, and do what I say I'm going to do, on time, because I have empathy for my audience's perspective and I always expect that that is what everybody will do … except they don't, which is disappointing. I don't understand hidden meanings, implied meanings, double meanings and sarcasm because I receive, process and respond to information in a straightforward, unemotional way.

That's why I communicate well with children.

But it makes me the alien in the room.

It means I need a lot of time and space alone in my empty jar, to recover from communicating with adults, and to prepare for more.

Something I find hard to grasp is when people replace the actual time with vague words. They might say 'see you *soon*,' 'I'll ring you *in a bit*,' 'talk to you *later*,' 'call you *at some point*.' If someone says to me 'I'll ring you *in a bit*' I take this as the instruction: be ready for my phone call *in a bit*. I don't know when *in a bit* actually is, so I put everything on hold and I am anxious in case I miss their call. Sometimes *in a bit* means in five minutes, sometimes it can be five hours, and sometimes it's apparently just another way of saying 'goodbye.'

I spent all day, phone in hand, waiting for that call.

After that I was called "silly."

*"What do you think you are doing?"* asked my Year Five teacher when I was eating the class fruit underneath the table. (She had earlier told me that she didn't want to *see* me eating the class fruit during class time, hence why I was under the table.) When I told her "I am eating the class fruit" she told me off for "being smart." I still don't really know, to this day, what the correct answer to her question would have been. I thought *"being smart"* was the overall aim of attending. My confusion, mixed with the knowledge that I hadn't pleased her, has remained with me for my entire life.

I now know that *"What do you think you are doing?"* means *"keep quiet because you're in deep trouble."* It's a bit like *"Who do you think you are?"* They never really wanted an answer to that either.

As a teacher, my primary classroom functioned because no child was confused about what I wanted them to do and how I wanted them to do it. I could adapt how I explained things. Some children responded well to repetition, some needed models and demonstrations, some needed time to explore an idea practically, on their own, some needed visual instructions and explanations. I was consistent in this with all thirty children because I know what it's like to misunderstand. My communication ethos with the children stayed the same regardless of time, my mood, my job-load, and my responsibilities, because I hated the thought of them feeling the anxiety and isolation of misunderstanding. If I can do this for thirty children at once, you can do it for one autistic person.

Anxiety is a big cause of misbehaviour; misbehaviour is either an expression of distress or a way of distracting people from realising that you don't understand. The pressure, mixed with embarrassment, of not-understanding is difficult to face. No-one has the time or inkling to misbehave for no reason. As an autistic adult, it is degrading to feel confused about things that other adults just accept and 'just know'. Especially when it regards the language I have spoken since birth and studied at university. If people are communicating with me in ways I cannot understand it will affect my behaviour toward them as a means of protecting my pride as an adult.

Many people think I am shy but I am just careful. Some people think I am anti-social but this is also inaccurate. I love people but I love talking about real, honest stuff, not the bloody weather conditions. We can all see what the weather is doing. What is the purpose of talking about the weather other than to fill a beautiful silence? People think I am blunt but really I am just saving them from the trauma of misunderstanding. People think I am quiet but the truth is that I'm not good at opening or closing conversations, and it doesn't occur to me to talk when there is nothing to say.

I haven't switched off, I haven't misheard. I literally haven't understood the abstract way in which people communicate when they reach adulthood. It means I focus on facts like who, when, what, where, why. It *should* give me a less cloudy view of the social world and human relationships, but it doesn't.

I got a text message this morning saying "*It's nice today, isn't it.*" I had no idea what it was referring to, yet I also knew that my friend had left the subject out on purpose because I was supposed to 'just know'. My response was "yes" because it seemed (from the pressing "isn't it") that was the answer she wanted.

Whilst verbal communication is the most efficient means of communication for humans worldwide, this is not true for me or for many autistic people. I don't talk without intention, I don't think aloud and expect a response. I communicate more effectively in other ways, but the world isn't ready to accommodate this yet. Now that people are using their phones to text how they speak, texting and instant-messaging are also becoming problematic for some autistics.

It's hard to understand the parts of sentences people leave out.

*"Come round for a coffee whenever you like,"* really means *"Come round for a coffee whenever you like ... but not on Wednesdays because that's when I do the shopping, and not when I'm in a bad mood because I'll sit dropping hints that I want you to go."* It is confusing when you pick the 'wrong time' to go round for coffee, even though it was suggested that there would *never* be a 'wrong time'. It would be easier to say 'ring me when you would like to come here for coffee, and I will let you know if it's a good time.'

But even then, it will be difficult to instigate that conversation. *'Come around for coffee today at midday for two hours'* would be a secure invitation.

My social and communication difficulties border on fear most of the time because I am self-aware. I am conscious of my deficits in communication and constantly worried that I haven't picked up on the things people *haven't* said. "I can't find my keys" really means "please can you help me find my keys?" But I don't pick up on this passivity and this is when I am deemed rude and lacking in empathy. Just ask me if I can help you find your keys! Tell me how you are feeling, what you need and what you want.

I feel like an intruder, everywhere I go.

The minute I arrive somewhere, I am looking for hints that might be telling me to leave, because many non-autistic people hint. If someone asks me if I would like a drink, I'm not sure if they would rather I said yes or no. Would they rather I don't use up their teabags? I don't know. Are they just being polite by offering and hoping I say no? Should I be able to tell this by the tone of their voice, the look in their eye, the shape of their mouth or the way they're leaning against the doorframe?

I don't trust people to just *say what they mean*, so I am always over-thinking and checking, which people then find annoying. I have a lifetime of social misunderstandings in my memory though, and a desire to be liked and to do the right thing.

Autism is a social and communication disability that presents itself in many different ways, but we still all have a need to communicate, even if we are completely non-verbal. We might communicate through film quotes, drawings, dance, choreography, song lyrics, numbers, poetry, writing letters, fictional characters, in how we move or by doing things *for* people. You have to find out how your autistic person communicates best, and listen. Sometimes you will need to listen with your eyes rather than with your ears, but what you 'hear' will never be sugar-coated with any extra layers of meaning, it will just be real and rare.

Many autistic people are very verbal and verbally confident, and their autism shows itself in different ways. But even the most talkative autistic person can become overwhelmed and shut down. Talking is the first thing to go when I am struggling with communication overload.

Autism is an explanation, not an excuse. But it is nice to know who we can turn to when things aren't making sense. It is nice to know who values what we have to say, even if we don't say it in the conventional way.

# A Roar of Triumph

I had an excellent time in London with Jack and Dan when we went to see the autism-friendly performance of *The Lion King* at the Lyceum Theatre in London.

It was outstanding.

I felt so special attending this unique show. Autistic people have to adapt to fit in to this world every day, so what a delightful treat to have something adapted for us.

We waited outside in the fresh air before finding our seats in the busy auditorium.

A man called Santiago checked our tickets on the door.

The theatre was beautifully grand: I had already looked at pictures of it online because I hadn't been there before, and I wanted to be prepared. It was more beautiful in real life of course. Our seats were splendid and close to the stage. As we sat down together, I had no worries. This was an extraordinary feeling for me to have in a public place, surrounded by people. My body was relaxed and being itself: the noises from the people around me gave me comfort and told me that they were all being themselves too.

The Lion King has been my favourite Disney movie since I was nine years old.

Hakuna Matata – no worries – for sure.

*I realised that in here, I wouldn't have to apologise for being me.*

All of the cast, crew and theatre staff had received autism training. There were people dotted around everywhere from the National Autistic Society and from Disney, wearing clearly marked T-shirts. They were trained and ready to help if we needed anything before, during, or after the performance, and they all looked so eagerly friendly.

There were designated chill-out areas in quiet zones, to be used if we needed a break. Adaptions had been made in the toilets. Theatre staff held up visual instructions on enormous signs telling us to switch off our phones, and that taking videos and photographs was prohibited. I wished that instructions could *always* be given like this, so that if you don't quite understand, or you have too much information to process, or big announcements are too loud, you don't have to worry about asking somebody to repeat an instruction.

You just *look* again.

*It put me at ease that I was in the right place, doing the right things, independently.*

Just before the show was about to start, the auditorium door at the right-hand-side of the stage opened and two of the main characters walked in.

It was Scar and Rafiki.

*I wondered if my eyes were tricking me.*

They walked up and down the aisles in the stalls, shaking people's hands. The ushers and theatre staff were telling us to look and people were pointing. Their make-up and detailed costumes were breathtaking.

I was *so* astonished.

Scar and Rafiki walked up onto the stage and talked to us all. Scar, in his magnificent voice, welcomed us. He explained that his name is really George Asprey, and that Scar is the character he plays. He told us that he is not really bad, just misunderstood, and that is sometimes how *I* feel! It made me laugh. It made me relax. It made me wish that the police officers with the guns in *Blood Brothers* had done that too, to remind us all that it is just acting.

Scar's speech was clear and caring. He told us that this was the fifth autism-friendly performance of *The Lion King*, and that they are honoured to do it. He introduced Rafiki, and he told us that she will be the first character we will meet when the show starts. I felt grateful to him for telling me what to expect next.

*It amused me that his most famous song is 'Be Prepared,' and he was the one preparing us ...*

The house-lights dimmed but remained on. This meant I could still see what was going on around me, and remember that I was sitting between my two friends. The noise from the audience continued as Rafiki sang *Nants ingonymama bagithi Baba,* telling us in her Zulu language that a lion is coming.

*I glanced over my shoulder as the saffron sun rose over Pride Rock.*

I could hear non-verbal autistic adults and children squealing repetitively, communicating their wonder and overload. There were people everywhere wearing ear defenders of many colours. Nobody was trying to quieten their physical or verbal stimming. For once our differences were socially acceptable. There was hand-flapping, wailing, clapping, spinning, rocking, intermittent explosive screams of joy and overwhelm. There were autistic adults clutching comforters, parents praising, reassuring and explaining. Everyone was free and welcome. People were making their own noises to drown out the new, unfamiliar ones. People were making friends. A teenage boy walked past me wearing a T-shirt that said 'I just really like musicals'. Every time a song finished, the little boy sitting in front of us would throw his arms around his mum's neck and kiss her on the lips. Nothing beats autistic joy.

*No-one was going to judge anyone for being 'different' or 'disruptive'.*

*It was liberating.*

I did not have to sit and struggle because the lights were too bright or because it was too loud. The National Autistic Society had worked in tandem with the show to assess all of these things, and adjust them for an autistic audience. I did not have to worry that there would be unexpected pyrotechnics, explosions and strobe lighting. I would have felt able to leave the auditorium for a break without feeling weird, isolated, embarrassed, judged, weak, guilty, paranoid or stupid, knowing that somebody would have helped me.

There was so much that I loved.

I loved *He Lives In You*, because it reminded me of when I sang it in Love Soul Choir: it reminded me of the passion I had when I taught it to the children in singing assemblies, and it reminded me of all the people that live *in me. Can You Feel The Love Tonight* was so believably romantic. Nala singing *Shadowlands* was one of the best things I have ever seen live.

I watched every intricate piece of lioness-choreography and paid attention to every costume detail. Zazu made me laugh the most. The animals that walked down the aisles took my breath away: I didn't know if I was afraid or in awe of the elephants, the giraffes, the antelopes, the birds. I just wanted to know how the costumes worked.

My favourite character was Scar.

The theatre is my favourite place in the world. I love to see shows as much as I can, but I am normally the biggest actor of them all: suppressing my stims; masking my sensory difficulties; ignoring my boiling-quiet autistic anxiety. It physically hurts to mask it all the time, and you can't take off the mask at the end of the show when your whole life is a show.

I only felt pride there, in the Lyceum Theatre.

I felt proud of myself and the other autistic people: proud of our wonderful, patient friends and families; proud of the theatre cast, crew and staff for learning about what it is like to be autistic, and proud of Chris Pike - the autism access specialist - and the National Autistic Society for making the theatre experience magical and accessible.

From where I sat, it was a roaring success. I have found where I belong, and it feels marvellous.

Nothing beats autistic joy.

# My Quest for Detail

If I had to describe Autism using only three words, I would say 'quest for detail.' If I were given the option to continue my life without autism I would decline, now that I have taken the time, with therapy, to explore all the difficulties and discover all the positives, because I would never want to give up my quest for detail and the joy and richness it brings me in my everyday life and in my job.

Sometimes the world seems more alive for me than it does for other people.

Some of the best things I have ever created have come from my blessed autistic brain.

Yes, I strive for perfection. I have high expectations for myself and others. I hyper-focus. I overwork. I find moderation extremely difficult. I analyse and obsess over things, but I am not really talking about this kind of detail. This kind of detail is conscious. It comes from perfectionism, obsession, pressure, anxiety, choice, not autism.

The kind of detail I am talking about is my ability to absorb such intricacy from my environment, and the inability to filter out anything that is irrelevant to me in that moment. Everything wants to be noticed by me. Everything wants to be heard by me, smelt by me, touched, tasted, and everything is detailed and amplified. This can be overwhelming, as I have explained previously. It can be distracting and weird for the people around me, but it can also bring me joy and a drive and ability to put that extra detail back into the things I create myself.

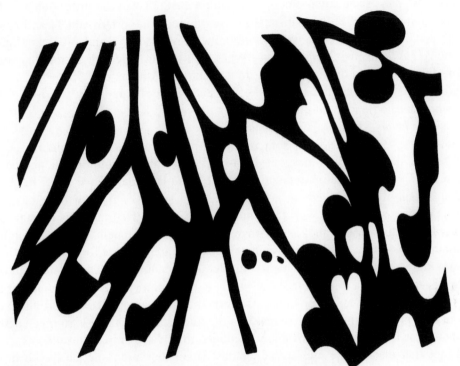

It's being so observant that you see
the pattern on the wing of a butterfly
before you realise that it's a butterfly.

*I am an observer, thereby a learner, and that is my permanent state - Ralph Waldo Emerson.*

I may not walk into a room and 'see the bigger picture'. I may not 'suss things out' and 'get the gist' like other people do. Everything needs to be pieced together like a puzzle before I can process an environment in its entirety, and this has an impact on how I am able to communicate, especially with adults. Everything is important and I can't 'zoom out'. Other people do the opposite, with more immediacy but less wonder. Naoki Higashida, in his book *The Reason I Jump*, writes: 'When you see an object, it seems you see it as an entire thing first, and only afterwards do its details follow on. But for people with autism, the details jump straight out at us first of all, and then only gradually, detail by detail, does the whole image float up into focus.'

*I would be an excellent CCTV camera.*

Of course this overloads me sometimes. It affects my motor skills and my sense of the feelings inside my body. It makes it extra-hard to socialise, communicate and concentrate. It is even harder to socialise and communicate in a place that I have never been to before, because then my brain needs to notice everything and everyone for the first time, but it makes me see magic in the world that others don't notice. That magic is far superior to any difficulties autism brings and, once I have absorbed all that magic, I can use it in my lesson planning, my writing, my choreography projects, my art, my love for people.

My quest for detail means I learn a lot that I never forget, because once I have seen or heard even the tiniest thing, it is stored safely in my memory like a photograph or a podcast that I can refer back to. If something interests me, I am compelled to find out every detail about it. It is comforting for me to research my interests when there is so much about 'being human' that I seem to 'just *not* know'. I notice tiny changes in environments, people and routines that disorientate me, no matter how small they are. I notice the scent of an air freshener that's been sprayed in a room and settled on a blanket, the individual hairs on a person's head, the sound of electricity.

Other people do this too, often with less intensity and the ability to filter it all out when someone talks to them.

My quest for detail is conscious and subconscious. It affects my ability to socialise, communicate and function amongst people who do not realise that this is what my brain contends with. But it means that my daily life, and the daily lives of the people I share my experiences with, can never be boring.

Therein lies the cure for my depression.

People forget that there are positives to being super sensitive. Those that think you are 'fussy' when you are experiencing sensory things in a negative way, forget that you will experience the opposite end of hyper-sensitivity too, and that's brilliant. You see, hear, smell, taste, create and love in extra detail which opens you up to a myriad of desirable talents that benefit the world.

# 'Living with' Autism

It's funny when people ask what it's like to 'live with' autism. I get an image of a little house-elf called 'Autism' following me around my home, sharing my spaces, longing to be free.

It's not really like that. I don't 'live with' autism, in the way that you can 'live with' a broken leg, or a boyfriend. Gay people don't 'live with gay' and you wouldn't describe a Chinese person as 'living with Chinese'. I am entirely autistic, but I am not a broken leg. Autism is present in everything I see, say, smell, hear, feel and think: it is in everything I do, everywhere I go, and in every decision I make. *I can't move out and leave it behind.*

As an adult I have had to move house eight times due to contracts and relationships ending. Never through choice.

That is eight times in ten years (since leaving various student accommodations and qualifying as a primary school teacher) that I, and my bubbling undiagnosed, unmanaged autism, have moved house. I have '*lived with*' a housemate, with friends, in a shared house with strangers, with a boyfriend and on my own. I have never felt 'at home' and often felt *alone*, despite living in all of these places 'with autism'.

Until recently, I had no idea just how much of an impact my home environments have on me. Being autistic means the world is on full-blast, twenty-four hours a day. So being able to escape to a safe haven of controlled comfort is *vital* for my physical and mental wellbeing. Home needs to be a secure place, where I can be my true self, to stim, engage in whatever feels safe, to recharge my batteries enough to be able to cope with more 'world'.

Your secure will be different to *my* secure.

Everyone's paradise is different.

Clutter just clutters-up my already-busy brain. It suffocates my vision, causes unnecessary additional sensory-stress. I need white walls and minimalism, fresh air and natural or soft lighting, space, subtle room-sprays, cleanliness. Not too many material things. My brain needs to feel like it can catch its breath when it gets home. Flowers are the only bright things I can tolerate. I adore flowers; they please my senses, aromatically and aesthetically. They are soft and kissable, inimitable, natural.

Secure means no-one knocking my door or calling the house-phone. It is free of unpredictability, noises and conflict. Everything needs to work, because life is hard enough. I need to be able to be my true self. Only then can I recuperate my social stamina in order to function again in the outside world, like an outside human, with other humans.

This can make living with others extremely difficult.

● It is my guess that many autistic people will want to live alone, preferably on an island in the middle of nowhere unreachable by *any* other humans, unless by appointment. Many people with autism *do* live alone, successfully, with occasional support from carers or visitors. With hindsight from personal experience, there are important things to consider. Stereotypically, autistic people block out the world when focussed on a specific interest, potentially neglecting ordinary daily life. Combine this with poor executive function, lack of financial understanding and management, social masking, isolation or hidden mental health difficulties (or all of the above) and things can spiral out of control very quickly. You cannot see it when you are in it. Autistic people 'cope' in dire circumstances when we cannot communicate needs. Many autistics *do* live alone successfully, but it will be necessary for loved ones to pop in to check things from time to time.

● If you live alone 'with autism', ask an understanding friend to help you write a detailed, visual, daily routine to laminate and stick on your fridge. Your routine should include even the tiniest jobs, like brushing your teeth, switching off electrical appliances when they are not being used, closing/opening the curtains. It will be comforting to refer to this when you are overwhelmed or overloaded. Leave notes around the house in appropriate places that instruct you to do necessary things. Include timings. Have a standard, essential shopping list and meal plans you keep to weekly, but add extras when or if you fancy. A friend will help you know what needs to be done and when. Neuro-typical people tend to 'just know' these things rather better than we do. I don't think they even know that they know! Perhaps organise your shopping to be delivered to your home at the same time each week. After a while, household routines start to happen naturally, but you still need to keep the timetabled routine on your fridge. When your special interests or hyper-anxiety or executive functioning fail you, you will be glad to have things about you that give you instructions.

● Give someone you trust a spare key to your home in case you get locked out. This is wise for *everyone*, but of course I learned this lesson the hard way, twice. Communicating with a trusted key-holder is easier than communicating with a stranger or organising a locksmith over the phone.

● Keep a safe, somewhere safe. Not for money necessarily, but for personal information that you might not be able to remember all of the time. Things like passwords, email addresses, bank details. Share this information with one person you trust very much, or give them a spare key to the safe. Ask an organised friend to collate personal information with you if you are not sure what is relevant, and to help you make an alphabetised folder of important documents like contracts, car insurance, MOT certificates, passports etc. so that everything is organised and in one place. This will save you future anxiety when you need something quickly.

● Ask someone you trust to help ensure you have important numbers in your phone so that they are easily accessible. These could be the doctor, police, NHS direct, crisis team, therapist, hairdresser, landlord, your place of work, breakdown assistance etc. as well as numbers for friends and family. Make sure your number for breakdown cover is also in your car, in case your phone battery dies. Practise making telephone calls to these people using role-play. These kinds of communications can be exceptionally stressful for anyone, let alone someone on the autistic spectrum. Make an agreement with a close, trusted friend that you will call them when you need *any* kind of help. If you *are* the close, trusted friend, give praise when you are contacted. It is hard to instigate a conversation about the weather when you are autistic, let alone ask for *help*. Go so far as to write down what to say on the phone when you call. Agree it together. Practise it. Make it undoubtedly OK.

● Consider letting a neighbour know that you are autistic, and explain briefly what this means, so that there is someone close you can approach in a difficulty. Ask a friend to help you talk to them if this feels hard, or write them a little letter. It will be useful to swap telephone numbers with a neighbour if they agree to this. It doesn't mean you have to have them round for coffee; it's just a sensible safety measure.

● Choose to live somewhere that allows, or is suitable for, pets, for example a service dog, or any pet who is your best friend. Pets bring comfort and company. They can also help you realise your purpose and feel needed. Dogs need to be exercised and this will help with your own physical and mental fitness. They may sleep with you at night, calm you when you hear strange noises, temporarily redirect your attention onto something different if you are hyper-focussed, 'ground' you, give you more confidence to go out to public places, and just be really glad to see you when you get home. Pets are easy to talk about in social situations where you don't know what to say.

● Make sure that at least once a week you have somewhere to go instead of staying at home. This can be a visit to family or a friend. It could be a hobby you enjoy, like photography or running or music. It is tempting to disappear when you live alone: binge-watch *Grey's Anatomy*, clean obsessively, live in your pyjamas. But this is not healthy for the stimulation of your mind or your sense of self-worth. If your autistic friend lives alone, or spends a lot of time alone, and you haven't seen them lately, find a way to get in touch with them. Things can spiral out of control very quickly. *You cannot see it when you are in it.* Autistic people 'cope' in dire circumstances when we cannot communicate needs. Social media *isn't real contact* and it isn't enough. If your autistic person is socially isolating themselves, try a new angle – ask them to do you a practical favour, something that helps you and makes them feel needed and important.

● Write yourself a list of instructions about how to calm down when you are feeling too anxious and overloaded. Stick this to the wall in a calm area of your home. These instructions can include things that enable you to ground yourself and remain calm in stressful times. A list like this will be different for everyone and if you're like me, it will take you ages to find out what your soothing strategies are, but it is important for balance. Make sure your sensory items are easily accessible and get into the habit of using them to prevent overload, not just calm it down. It is also worthwhile to keep a diary. This doesn't need to be detailed if you're not a writer, but it is a tool to aid clear communication about your thoughts, feelings, worries, wants and needs, plans, health and how you are spending your time. It could even be visual, like drawings, photographs or comic strips. You can take it to psychiatrist's and doctor's appointments for example, to take the pressure off you and your verbal communication skills in these pressured circumstances.

● All of the above points are also relevant if you live with a friend or family. They are all still relevant and necessary tips to live successfully 'with autism' whatever your circumstances and I am sure you can think of more. If you *do* share your home, it will be important to ensure your housemates respect your need for quiet and space. *There should be a calm, safe, private place within the house that is yours,* where you can close your eyes, sit, lie, breathe, loosen your clothes, count, repeat, stim, rock, drink water, cry, hum, recharge, remind yourself of what needs to happen next, recover, be present, do whatever is personally necessary to continue with your day. This space will be where you feel relaxed, and where you can keep your sensory objects. You need to be in control of how the space looks and how it is organised.

> *Be careful who you choose to live with. For many reasons, autistic people are vulnerable to abuse. Some of these reasons include a tendency to follow instructions; eagerness to please and to 'fit in'; a lack of social skills and knowledge about what is acceptable behaviour from others. Autistic people can be easy to take advantage of. They have a tendency to be trusting and very loyal. Communication difficulties and fear of change, along with the unpredictability of help might mean that if an autistic person feels like they are in trouble, they will tolerate it rather than tell someone.*

# The Chapter That Was Missing

I submitted the manuscript for *Too Much World* to my editor and it was returned to me, after just a few days, with astute alterations, positive comments and the suggestion to include a chapter about love.

It *did* feel like the book was obviously 'missing something' without a chapter about the lived experiences of an autistic person in love, but it was a chapter I had left out deliberately. My entire existence revolves around creating order in a world that is already confusing enough, without adding in complex emotions like *love*.

I agreed that I would do it.

So far my longest relationship has been with alcohol and I have managed, lately, to convince psychology professionals that my relationship with alcohol is *good*. It seems to give me everything I need from a relationship. It dulls my senses making everything less sharp like noise, light and anxiety. Less anxiety means my reactions to stimuli are more normal. It tunes out the bad thoughts and replaces them with more encouraging ones, increasing my confidence, whilst allowing me to drop the mask and be my authentic self. The frequency of which I drink alcohol has, in the past, made professionals label my drinking "problematic" although I never get drunk, due to the fact that I dislike the feeling of being out of control. I schedule 'time off' two to three days in the week so that my liver can have the time and space it needs to function effectively, and I never drive if I have been drinking, which shows respect. I wouldn't drink late on a school night like other teachers do, and I don't buy expensive alcohol, which shows that I *do* possess some skills with regards to money management. In conclusion my relationship with alcohol is made up of thought, truth, appreciation, and (appropriately scheduled) pleasure, which – for me – are the ingredients of love.

The trouble is, everyone needs *different* ingredients. You have to find out what those ingredients are and use *their* ingredients in order to make a relationship last.

Relationships with other humans involve slick social and emotional communication skills, including the verbal ability to share your wants and needs and fulfil them for others, alongside using positive body language, adopting an appropriate tone, flirting and other verbal/non-verbal oddities.

I've been in a few relationships in my life, none of which I look back on with regret because every single one of them taught me something valuable. My only regret is that, despite somehow knowing that I wasn't ready for some of these relationships, I went ahead with them anyway, and tried to make them work by being like other girls. I wasn't fulfilling the needs of the boyfriend I was with because I wasn't picking up the hints and clues that would have told me what these needs were ... and I didn't know why. I wasn't effectively communicating my own needs and feelings because I had no idea myself what they were. I had no idea what I wanted from the relationship, or that my *wants* might differ from the other person's ideals, and I found myself trying to love in ways that were never quite appreciated.

These are things that can be difficult to communicate and build on in any relationship, let alone a relationship in which one of the people is autistic.

Although I had no idea I was autistic, I frantically tried to hide my worries and differences because I thought that would give me more of a chance to be loved.

Of course that was never going to work – that's obvious now.

I suppose it scared me that I might *never* succeed in a relationship, so I ended up saying 'no' eight times to someone I really liked, who would come into the bar where I worked and write me love notes on the back of receipts. I still have them. Eventually, he became fed up with asking me out and being rejected, so we became good friends despite knowing that there was 'something there'. I don't often 'get' jokes or find comedy funny but he was constantly making me laugh. I didn't like the taste of beer, but it tasted marvellous when I drank his. I was a stickler for rules but I *enjoyed* breaking them with him. Being with him energised me – it felt *natural*. For the first time ever, I was spending most of my free time with another human without the pressure of trying to be someone I wasn't.

We seemed to be speaking the same language.

Whatever that feeling was, it frightened the life out of me. To this day I wouldn't have the confidence to identify it accurately. In the aftermath of his death, his friends told me that in his own words it had been *love,* but I never heard him say that. Finally, we got together but fear (probably) eventually came between us again and we both ended up in separate, happy relationships but maintained our close friendship.

We got back together the night that he died.

He came to me at the bar, turned me round, and I just kissed him. He lifted me up and I wrapped my legs around his body. Someone pulled the flower out of my hair as they walked by us, but I didn't stop kissing him. We made arrangements to go back to his house, but the arrangements didn't happen because a friend needed my help, so we said we'd see each other the next day.

Seventeen minutes later he was dead.

I could not process it. I still can't. I worked harder and helped those around me that *could* communicate their feelings. I learned to cook, because I wanted people to be filled up with something good.

But my belief that I was a bad person intensified.

Fast-forward five years and I am living with a new boyfriend in a lovely house. He is the most loving person that I have ever met, and I tell him that every day because time is precious. There is something *different* about him too. He hurts me in all kinds of ways when he is sad and drunk, because I am bad (in his words I am "*cancer,*") but he is also gentle and always there for me afterwards to make it better. I am 'rescued' from this relationship two months after running away from my home, by a man who treated me like a princess for six months, and then disappeared one evening while I was washing-up, and never contacted me again.

That was when my manic obsession with work increased.

# What Autistic People May Need You to Know about Relationships

PLANNING: The process of planning, on my own, is a means to decrease anxiety because it allows me to visualise ahead and feel in control. The process of planning with someone *else*, or following someone else's plan, increases my anxiety. My reaction to a plan made with or by another person might seem hesitant or unenthusiastic, but I am none of these things – I am just anxious. I need a bit of extra time alone to process someone else's plan and settle it down in my mind before I can be keen about it.

SURPRISES: I do not like surprises … but if the other person *does* like surprises, I will take pleasure in organising surprises for them. I need to know exactly what is going to happen, and when, all of the time. Even if someone were to surprise me by doing my favourite thing – like a trip to the theatre to see *Wicked* – I will not remember that that is my favourite thing in that moment. My anxiety will be greater than the show, and it will feel traumatic.

DIRECT COMMUNICATION: I don't pick up on social hints, cues and non-verbal communications as well as most people. I hear things literally and respond well to direction. Therefore I appreciate it when people communicate the things they want and need very clearly. Helpful statements like 'I feel loved when you compliment me,' 'I feel loved when you do things for me,' 'I feel loved when you buy things for me,' 'I feel loved when you touch me,' 'I feel loved when we spend time together…' etc. make me feel secure, and I will be delighted to respond to this information. Otherwise I will make it up and get it all wrong.

SOCIALISING AND SPACE: My 'social battery' runs out more quickly than most other people's. Some people are energised by spending time with others, whereas I need a lot of time and space alone in order to re-energise. My spending time alone does not mean I am not interested in spending time with you – it means I am re-charging from previous socialising, and getting ready to spend time with you as my best sociable self. The more pressure I feel when I am with someone, the more time I tend to need to myself afterwards.

SLEEP: Sleep is a nightmare for many people, especially those with anxiety or those on the autistic spectrum with sensitivity. There are so many things that prevent me from sleeping without medication: the feel of the bedding, the weight of the bedding, the temperature, noises, movements, the 'wrong' lighting, the position of the bed, vivid dreams, over-thinking today, worrying about tomorrow, and so much more. If things are not 'right,' it can be easy for the other person in the relationship to feel offended or rejected if we don't go to bed, or if we sleep in another room sometimes, but actually we are probably reacting as you would do if you swapped brains with us for a night.

SEX: '*Autistic people don't have sex ... autistic people don't like to be touched ... autistic people are not affectionate blah, blah ...*' I've heard it all! I expect there are some autistic people in the world who don't have sex, who don't like to be touched and who are not affectionate, (just as there are some non-autistic people who don't enjoy these things) but mostly the wants and needs of autistic people with regards to physical relationships are the same as those of most humans. Physical touches to the skin, certain textures and labels etc can feel painful to some autistic people (they feel painful to me in times of stress) but emotional, physical touching with a person you love or trust can be as pleasurable to us as it is to others.

CERTAINTY: I like it when things stay the same. I like doing familiar things and being in familiar places. This means I would be content to have the same date, in the same place, on the same night of the week, for the rest of my days. It would also mean that I am more focussed on the *person* I am with because the environment has already been processed. Other people are far more adventurous: they like new places, different places. They get bored with doing the same things over and over again. It is important to have compromise and show willing in every relationship – it just might take a little bit of extra time, research and patience to do 'new' things if you are dating an autistic person who needs certainty (and going on holiday might be challenging), but anything can happen with the right people and very careful planning.

STIMMING AND SPECIAL INTERESTS: The intensity with which I engage with the things that interest me is stronger than the focus my non-autistic friends give to their interests and hobbies. Many autistic people have interests that they become an 'expert' in: it enables them to escape from the social world into a world in which, for once, they hold all the knowledge and understanding. I am emotionally attached to my special interests and finding out more about them gives me rare comfort. I need my special interests to be respected when I am in a relationship and I might need to talk about them a lot. Similarly, I need my stimming behaviours to be accepted. Stimming helps me to think and regulate strong emotions and, although it might not seem socially acceptable, it is crucial to my mental health.

# What Strengths do Autistic People Bring to Relationships?

FIRST OF ALL, I AM NOT ACTUALLY AN ALIEN …

… in fact the idea of being seen as 'alien' is offensive to me. I am not a robot, a cat, a caterpillar, an owl, a hedgehog, a chair or any of the other things I have attempted to compare myself to in order to try to explain life as I know it. I have a few differences because I am an autistic woman, but mostly I am reliable, loyal, compassionate, tolerant, accepting, courageous and interesting.

RELIABILITY: Autistic people tend to be exceptionally reliable – we say what we mean, we do what we say we are going to do and respond, with pace, to direct instructions. Apparently, this is a strength, but I cannot imagine saying something I don't mean, or *not* doing something I have said I will do. I am a safe, honest and trustworthy person to rely on, and it doesn't occur to me to be any other way.

LOYALTY: Autistic people are very loyal and we demonstrate our loyalty in the things we willingly do for others. This willingness to support others is genuine. When difficulties arise within a relationship, autistic people want to solve the problem logically in a non-blaming way. We want to really understand it, and fix it, so that it is better for *both* sides. We are non-judgmental about people, just problems, and are willing to listen and try different solutions without taking things personally, or letting emotional reactions cloud the issue.

EMPATHY & COMPASSION: Autistic people don't just notice other people's negative emotions (fear, anger, sadness) we *absorb* them. When someone I love is struggling, I find it very hard to do *anything* until their feelings are better. This means that I will do my best, with compassion, to help them through difficult times, not only to calm *their* feelings but to calm the feelings I am having in sympathy for them.

SEEING THINGS DIFFERENTLY: When autistic people share their experiences of the world with their loved ones, we are giving others the opportunity to see things differently, to think differently and to notice things they may not have otherwise noticed. This can be fascinating and useful to people and it can also make them laugh. The world doesn't give much to autistic people, but autistic people give to the world every day.

TOLERANCE AND ACCEPTANCE: Autistic people are the most tolerant and accepting people in the world. We see through things that don't make sense and things that don't really matter, with a kind of logical innocence. Being autistic means that people make assumptions about us all the time and these assumptions are normally incorrect. Having assumptions made about you is hurtful, and we don't want other people to experience this hurt, so we are tolerant and accepting of everyone.

COURAGE: We've got to be brave to be autistic. Trying our best to succeed in the world when we feel things differently, communicate differently and think differently is incredibly difficult. Trying our best to succeed in a relationship, despite the difficulties we've faced in the past, and *know* we will face in the future, opens us up to an enormous amount of vulnerabilities and is just extremely courageous.

# Autism is a Blessing

Autism is reliable. Autism is polite. It is caring, considerate. It is putting others before yourself. Autism is loyalty. Autism is literal. Logical. It is lines, lists, links. Autism is observant. It is a brighter, extra-detailed perspective of the world. Another angle. A magic window. Autism is intelligent. It is eye-opening. It dissects. Invents. Discovers. Creates. It is having an awareness of the more unusual things in life. It sees a simpler picture. Appreciates the smaller things, the finer details, and the deeper meanings. Autism is super-sensitivity. Neurodiversity. It hypnotises. It has an extraordinary memory. It is kind, generous and direct. It is something different every day, but it is always everything amplified.

Autism is illuminating. It is wonder. It is uncompromisingly moral. Autism thinks around corners. It bends ideas. It thinks backwards. It allows me to see obvious solutions to problems. It is the 'hyper-focusability' needed to make the solution a reality. It is creativity. Dedication. Expertise. Autism is art. Autism is the quest to achieve knowledge of the subject I have chosen. It is individual. Beautiful chaos. Autism is true. It is pure, delicate and vulnerable. Autism is crystal-clear. It encourages others to be patient, gracious and accepting. It is a gift. A gentle light. Genetic. Autism is talent. It is diverse and exciting. It is needed. It is a best friend.

Autism is passion. Perseverance. Difference. It is the ability to focus intensely. It is refreshing non-conformity. Vivid dreams. Bravery. Strength. Autism is powerful. It is thinking in pictures, and bringing the pictures to life. Autism is life, unfiltered. Colours. Sounds. Experiences. It is real, raw, close, and honest. Autism is honesty. Brutal honesty. Clarity. Empathy. Bliss. Autism doesn't miss a trick. It is patterns in nature. Shiny paper. Ripples in a swimming pool. Leaves on your cheek. Autism is a teacher. A student. It is a daily reward. A privilege.

Autism is story making. A wild imagination. It is song lyrics. Names. Words. It is painting, poetry and perfume. Autism is routines and blankets. Patterns. Rhythms. Repetition. Black and white. It is smells and breathing, and spending time alone. Autism is making comparisons. Making connections, not making connections. Autism is a profound

connection with animals. An affinity with objects. It is nothing sugar-coated.

Autism is affectionate. Autism is loving. Lovable. Autism feels everything more. More love. More joy. Closer friendships. Autism is appreciative. Fair and just. It is a series of behaviours adopted to create order in a seemingly disordered world. Autism is structure. Security. Truth. It sees through bullshit. Autism is never being bored. Life's answer to monotony. Autism is innocent. Autism asks questions. It finds answers. Facts. It is starting a job and seeing it through to the end. It is intense productivity. Motivation. Stamina. Autism makes sense. Autism is normal. It is someone safe.

Autism, in its best light, is being neuro-fascinated by the world around you.

But you don't need to be autistic to be neuro-fascinated.

When you switch off the 'social' you see more, naturally. You realise that there is more to life than you can ever imagine. There is more to touch, taste, feel, hear, and smell. There is deeper pain, greater joy, colder cold. There is more light, more colour, more detail. When you switch off the 'social' a million extra lights come on, like stars, shining, in your mind.

# Dear Saffie Cat

Dear Saffie Cat,
I've got my job back.
I thought I would never do it, but I have.
I've joined the gym, I'm in a new relationship,
I'm working with a new NHS mental health team
that are doing a great job of helping me.
I am considering going back to choir, to sing!
Now I realise, that this all needed to happen
because I had so much to learn
in order to be able to manage this life.
I am so glad to be alive, Saffie.
I've got this now, we've got this.
Thank you for listening my girl.

This crusade to fix herself was ending right now.
She wasn't broken.
She saw and interacted with the world in a different way
but that was her.
She could change her actions, change her words
change her appearance
but she couldn't change the root of herself.
At her core, she would always be autistic.
People called it a disorder, but it didn't feel like one.
To her it was simply the way she was.


Helen Hoang, *The Kiss Quotient*